No one who has traveled in Mexico asks who Benito Juárez was. His story is told on the painted walls; his statue stands in every city and in the plazas of small villages. From one end of the country to the other schools, colleges, and universities bear his name. Streets and broad boulevards are named in his honor along with the names of the other revolutionary heroes who brought the Mexican people the national independence they prize above all else.

Benito Juárez lived during the crucial period in Mexico's emergence as a democratically self-governing nation and, perhaps more than any other single individual, helped to shape its destiny.

With insight, understanding, and a highly developed sense of history, Emma Gelders Sterne has told the story of Benito Juárez, from his birth in an obscure Indian village through his entire lifetime of effort and achievement on behalf of his native land.

Benito Juárez

BENITO JUAREZ

Builder of a Nation

Emma Gelders Sterne

ILLUSTRATED BY RAY CRUZ

Alfred A. Knopf : New York

Acknowledgments

So many people, both in California and in Mexico, were of help to me in preparing this story of the life of Benito Juárez that it is impossible to name them all, but I would show myself ungrateful indeed if I failed to acknowledge the work of my friends Anne Rowe and Andrew Ramos. Mrs. Rowe acted as my tireless interpreter during my stay in Mexico and particularly during my two weeks in Oaxaca—in the mountain village where Benito Juárez was born and in the city where his presence is felt to this day. Andrew Ramos translated for me numberless passages from books in the Spanish language and from the notes Benito Juárez wrote for his children.

My thanks, too, to Señor Jorge Fernando Iturribarria of the Juárez University in Oaxaca and the leading historical authority on Juárez; to Señor Marcial Martinez Aquirre, and Señor Antonio Ramirez Lopez who spent hours with us in the National Juárez Museum in Mexico City; to Lena de Vries of Cuernavaca and her friend Professor Algo Melcher at the Juárez *Escuela*, which is built on the site of Benito Juárez's birthplace at Guelatao.

Finally, I must acknowledge debt for the historical facts of Benito Juárez's life to the authors of four books:

Helen Augur: *Zapotec*. New York: Doubleday & Company; 1954.

Ralph Roeder: *Juárez and His Mexico, a biographical history*. 2 vols. New York: The Viking Press, Inc.; 1947.

Justo Sierra: *Juárez, Su Obra y Su Tiempo*. Mexico City: University of Mexico, new edn.; 1956.

Charles Allen Smart: *Viva Juárez!* Philadelphia: J. B. Lippincott Co.; 1963.

CONTENTS

MEXICO

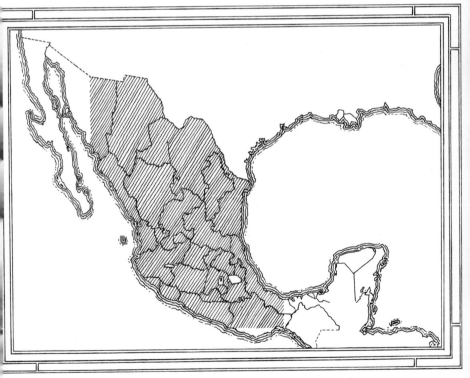

An enlargement of the shaded area appears on the facing page.

≪1≫

The Road from Guelatao

The bells! A deep, sonorous tolling; a clanging; now
a shrill patter light as the sound of rain on the mountain he had left behind him . . . The vesper bells of
Oaxaca's hundred churches were a burden on the ears
of the twelve-year-old boy standing bewildered on
the edge of the city's main plaza. From the cathedral
tower behind him, from the hills, from the black
shadows of buildings huddled together, from every
side came the clamor of the bells. This was a thing no
traveler had mentioned in answer to the boy's endless
questioning about the city in the valley.

Travelers' tales had made Benito Juárez familiar
with the double towers of the cathedral, where the
altar was said to be of pure gold. He knew that the
Royal Palace was the massive gray stone building
guarded by those Spanish soldiers in red-plumed helmets. Under the arched portals on three sides of the
plaza, he knew that you could buy all manner of

strange foods. The boy could see the little cakes on trays carried on the heads of the vendors, could smell delicious, smoky meat smells rising from braziers set close to the buildings. After his forty-mile walk down the mountain he was very hungry, but to buy you had to have coins in your pocket—which of course he hadn't. Benito Juárez in all his twelve years had never possessed a *peso* of his own.

At home in Guelatao money seldom passed in trading between men or women in the market. How could an orphan boy, depending on his uncle for food and shelter and the clothes he wore, come into possession of money? His uncle had very little himself. Any pesos that came to him from the sale of a sheep went into a leather bag to be given to the priest who came occasionally to their village to collect the church taxes, or to purchase a candle on feast days when the church was opened and one remembered the dead. Candles for his mother and his father; candles for the grandmother who had cared for him and his two sisters until she died. . . .

That was when his uncle had taken Benito into his house to live. An eight-year-old boy could make himself useful watching the sheep as they grazed on the tall grass growing by the Enchanted Lake. There were no womenfolk in the one-room house that had become his home. María, his older sister had married and gone off over the next mountain to the east. Josefa, his beloved sister Josefa, had run away to Oaxaca to become a servant in the household of the "foreigners." (This was how the Indians of Oaxaca thought of the Spaniards who three hundred years ago had seized and still held the land of their ancestors.) And yet, to become a servant to the Spaniards was the reason Benito Juárez had made the solitary journey down the mountain. It was one way—almost the only way, in fact—a Zapotec from the mountain villages could get an education.

In Oaxaca even a penniless boy could learn to read and write. A young priest from the big church in Ixtlan, an Indian of the Zapotec nation, had told him how this miracle was managed. You bound yourself for a number of years to work for the foreigners. In turn, the Spanish master had to promise to let you have hours off to go to the parish school.

"You scrub and sweep and cut firewood for the foreigners, but you are allowed to go to school." The young Zapotec priest had continued in a whisper, "Without education we cannot win our liberty. Padre Morelos says if you do not use your gifts, they go bad."

Morelos! Benito Juárez knew why the speaker had dropped his voice and looked around the tiny Guelatao plaza in fear of being overheard. It had been the year 1814, when José María Morelos was carrying on the rebellion Padre Hidalgo had started. Hidalgo's magnificent call for freedom and an end to foreign rule had united every Indian tribe; had made them realize they were one people. While Hidalgo was alive, victory seemed possible. But he had lived to lead the rebellion only one year. Padre Morelos had continued the revolution—had actually caused a constitution, a rule of government, to be written for the whole nation. He, too, was captured. He had been captured in the city of Oaxaca, excommunicated by order of the Inquisition, and shot close to Mexico City. It was forbidden by the Church to mention his name.

Benito Juárez, barefoot and hungry, standing bewildered and alone in the city around which his dreams had been woven—the dreams of "education and liberty" that were to be the lodestone of a long life—drew his grass cape closer around his shoulders. *If you do not use your gifts, they go bad* . . . His eyes wandered over the plaza with its spraying column of water in the center—the fountain—its gnarled laurel trees with flowers of blue and red. He studied the people moving in a constant stream along the paths.

Which of them knew his sister Josefa? How would he find her in this huge, confusing place of a hundred church bells? Their clamor was silenced now, but the confusion still surrounded the boy like a cloud.

If his uncle had only brought him to Oaxaca as he had promised, everything would have been easy. His uncle did not object to his schooling, but every year he had put Benito off. "Wait," the uncle had said. Who would tend the sheep if Benito went away?

"How could I wait any longer?" Juárez asked himself.

Then some muleteers coming up the mountain from Oaxaca stole a sheep from the flock. Benito had stopped them by the Enchanted Lake, as he stopped every stranger, to ask if they knew his sister.

"Are you from Oaxaca? Do you know Josefa Juárez? She works in the household of *Señor* Maza . . ."

He had learned the Maza name from a boy in the village who had seen Josefa in the market and had talked with her. And she had asked about her little brother.

The muleteers had never heard of Josefa. However, one of them had slyly kept Benito at the edge of the grazing field by talking to him. When they had gone, the shepherd boy missed the sheep. He had spent the night reproaching himself for his carelessness and thinking of the beating his uncle would give him in the morning.

"A beating I deserve," he had admitted to himself, sorrowfully. But there had been so many beatings . . . Before daybreak Benito had stuffed a cold *tortilla* into his pocket, put on his cape—which he had woven himself of the tall grasses around the Enchanted Lake —and crept from his uncle's hut onto the trail down the mountain.

By the time the sun was over the treetops, he had left the trail, for it was peopled with travelers going to

7

Oaxaca for the Feast of the Virgin of Soledad. He thought it best to keep out of sight for fear that someone from the village would see him and send him back to his uncle! He had gone all the way in a jog trot, hurrying along the bed of the stream, swiftly, silently toward his goal. "Education and liberty" . . . and Josefa! With such a destination in view, who would mind forty miles of rough going?

But he had not realized that a city was so big. The village of Guelatao had twenty families . . . You could stand in the plaza—even on Saturdays, when everyone came to exchange what they had grown or woven—you could stand there and speak a name and the person you sought would be before you. Oaxaca must have a thousand houses—not stilt huts like his uncle's, but houses with plaster walls of pink and saffron and apple green, blue, and lavender, with iron balconies and gates of iron. Benito had seen them along the dusty streets as he walked through the crowds to the plaza. Any one of them might house Josefa. Who could tell?

With sudden determination, he plucked at the black flowing sleeve of a passing priest.

"Padre, please, do you know my sister Josefa? From the village of Guelatao?"

The pale-faced priest looked down at the country boy. Zapotec, no doubt, from his high cheekbones and huge, sad eyes. Mixtecs had broader faces. The Spaniard did not understand the Zapotec language. He jerked his sleeve from Benito's grasp and hurried toward the cathedral. He was late for Vespers as it was.

The language! The priest had not even understood his question. This was a new problem for Benito Juárez to face. Across the plaza in front of the Palace, the plumes of the royal guard waved in the sunset. Knowledgeable no doubt, but they, too, were Spanish. In the land his forebears had inhabited for three thousand years, he was an alien.

"Your pardon." Benito's throat was dry as he bowed before a dark-skinned man in a frock coat walking slowly by, his hands behind his back. An official perhaps, but from the look of his face, an Indian. "Do you know Josefa? A servant in the house of Señor Maza?"

He got no further. The gentleman shook his head impatiently. He was indeed an Indian, but Mixtec was his language, not Zapotec.

The plaza was filled with people. Surely some of them spoke Zapotec! Benito hurried across the narrow cobbled street. Families, with children playing at the fountain's edge. A bootblack kneeling on the earth before the shoes of a soldier. Benito went from one to the other of the poorer, dark-skinned people, barefoot like himself. Some of them spoke Zapotec, but none of them knew his sister.

A boy with a flat wicker tray full of sweet cakes balanced on his head came across from the portal to sell his cakes. The smell, the delicious smell, made Benito gulp with hunger. He hesitated about stopping the boy because he could buy nothing. The boy brushed past to make a sale to two Spanish dandies in bright blue trousers.

A wizened old woman in black sat on the ground with country herbs and love potions spread out at her feet. From the way her *rebozo* was twisted into a turban, the long fringed ends of the scarf over each shoulder, Benito guessed her to be from his neighborhood.

"Your sister? From Guelatao? Pretty, you say, with braids laced with ribbons about her head? No, I don't know any Josefa. One I knew, a woman older than myself, but that was long ago."

"You are looking for Josefa Juárez?" the voice of the vendor of cakes broke in. "I know *Señorita* Josefa well. Just yesterday morning she came to my mother's market stall. She's very young to be a cook, but she knows how to buy food for the family she cooks for."

"My sister is already a cook?" Benito had heard that you only got to be a cook after many years of service. Perhaps this boy did not know Josefa after all.

"The Mazas are Italian . . . They don't care if she is young," the boy answered. "She had their little boy with her as usual—yellow hair, maybe five, six years old."

Benito Juárez was not interested in the Maza child. "Where? Where can I find Josefa?"

"The Mazas live out on the way to Monte Albán, on *Calle Isabella.*" The stranger was proud to give all this information, but Benito's face puckered in a frown. "Calle Isabella" meant nothing to him.

The boy pointed to a street sign across from the plaza.

I cannot read. I cannot even speak the Spanish tongue. Benito Juárez shook his head in frustration.

"Out that street," the boy pointed. "A house with a balcony. About a mile. The house is the color of ripe papaya fruit. If you look through the gate, you can see the patio. It's a big patio and even has a fountain. As I said, they are a rich family, the Mazas. Don't be afraid to ask."

Afraid? Benito Juárez had never been afraid in his life. His serious face broke into a smile. He hitched his cape over his shoulders. He had come this far toward his goal. What was one more mile?

≈2≈
Josefa

"A house the color of ripe papaya?" Benito Juárez stopped and peered up anxiously. He had come almost to the end of the street, but the gathering darkness had drained all color from the plaster walls. Still, he decided, this must be the Mazas' house. There was the iron balcony, and through the bars of the gate he could glimpse an open patio and hear the splash of water. He went closer. Yes, in the light of candles, like in a church, he could see a small fountain and flowers.

He looked around for a way to get inside. Somehow he could not bring himself to pull the cord on the bronze bell by the gate. But around the corner of the house, he saw a narrow passageway, and hesitantly made his way along it in the early December darkness. A square of light drew him on to an open door. A young woman in a bright blue shawl had her back to him. She stopped stirring the pot, and opened a door in the high, brick fireplace and drew out a steaming pudding. *Josefa? If the woman would only turn around, so I could see her face!*

Josefa Juárez was only eighteen, but the dignity of her position as cook in so fine a household made her seem older. As she busied herself with the Mazas' supper, she hummed a little tune. Like most Zapotecs, she loved music. Her bare feet moved back to the open grate, keeping time with the tune.

"More soup? Where do you put it all?" The words she spoke were Spanish, but the voice was unmistakable. Benito moved a step closer. Now he could see Josefa smiling down at a yellow-haired boy sitting at a table.

Her eyes were drawn to the doorway. Benito saw a startled look cross her face.

"Josefa! It's me. I have come."

"Benito . . ." Josefa almost dropped the soup bowl. Then she ran forward and he was in her arms. "Did Uncle Bernadino bring you? Did you come for tomorrow's fiesta?"

"No," he spoke shyly. "It is not like that at all." With her arms around him, his story came pouring out—the stolen sheep, the journey, the overwhelming bigness of Oaxaca, the difficulty of finding her. "It wasn't really the trouble about sheep, Josefa. I had to come for education and . . ." He did not speak the word "liberty," for he felt the blue eyes of the little boy staring at him. Liberty was not a thing you mentioned before foreigners.

It was Josefa who spoke the words, *education and liberty*. "Then news of Morelos' fight for independence has reached Guelatao? Did you find out that he was captured and killed? Did you know it was in Oaxaca that he was taken . . . ?"

"But, Josefa, is it not forbidden to speak the name of Morelos?"

Benito's sister laughed and said, "Not in this household. Señor Maza is not afraid. Hasn't he given his only son the patriot's name? José María . . ."

Benito interrupted. He had to explain his purpose in running away. "You must bind me to a master as his servant, Josefa. One who will send me to the parish school. That is the way it is done . . ."

"I know, I know what you want, little brother. Not that it is so easy to manage these things, not for an Indian, not for a servant girl—even a cook. But we'll find a way."

"What a strange-looking cape!" José María Maza had been quiet, examining the stranger with a small boy's intentness.

He climbed down from his chair and reached out to touch the dry, crackling grass garment. "Listen, Josefa, it sings!"

"The stranger is my brother, José María. *Es mi hermano*."

"*Hermano*—brother." Benito repeated and laughed. "Look, Josefa, already I can speak some Spanish. Does he like my cape? Tell him I will find some grasses and make one for him, though it will hardly go well with velvet suits and collars of lace. It is velvet, isn't it? I have seen cloth like that on the statue of the Virgin in the church."

"I like this boy," José said solemnly. "Can he stay and play with me?"

"He wants you to stay," Josefa translated hurriedly. Would there be a place for her brother in the Maza household? One of the stable-boys perhaps? Just for his keep, without wages? She looked from one boy to the other. The one so fair, the other so dark.

"Can I?"

Benito held his breath for his sister's answer. When it came it was not a simple yes or no. "Perhaps it can be managed," she said slowly. "You could sleep in the straw in the stable."

"Anywhere! Only don't send me back, Josefa. I must learn to read."

For several months Benito Juárez was part of the household of the warm, generous Maza family.

Antonio Maza was in many ways a remarkable man. Because he was himself a "foreigner"—neither part of the Spanish ruling class of churchmen or large land-owners, nor a *Creole* (a Spaniard born on Mexican soil), nor a *Mestizo* (of part Indian, part Spanish ancestry)—he saw clearly that the Indians, though neglected and despised, were the backbone of the New

Spain, the real creators of this outpost of civilization in the New World.

Señor Maza and his young wife had emigrated from Europe almost by accident. They had grown up in the days when the young Napoleon Bonaparte of France had come to Italy as a liberator. Napoleon had established a group of small republics across Italy. That was before the Frenchman had made himself Emperor and tried to bring all of Europe under his sway. The Mazas had wealth and a curiosity to travel. When things went badly in their country, they had hurriedly left for the New World.

Oaxaca was a showplace in New Spain when Antonio and his wife arrived in 1809. They decided to settle there and build their home in the Spanish style on the edge of the beautiful little city. But the peaceful time did not last. War followed them, it seemed. Even before the house was finished, news of Padre Miguel Hidalgo's uprising thundered throughout the colony.

Although Antonio Maza took no part in the rebellion, words such as "independence" and "liberty" did not frighten him. It was with regret that he saw the rebellion of 1810 go down to defeat.

The second try of the Mexican people—the rise of the mestizos and Indians under José María Morelos—touched him more closely because when Morelos came to Oaxaca, Maza saw firsthand the nobility of the man who tried to give Mexico a constitutional government.

When the Inquisition, long hated by moderate Italians, brought about the death of Morelos, he had grieved.

To desire freedom was to Maza a noble thing. He felt none of the fear and suspicion of Indians which the late rebellion had aroused among his Spanish friends. José María, named for Morelos, was Antonio's only child, and within reason he denied him nothing. The ragged young orphan who had come to Oaxaca for the sake of an education was made welcome. And not only to give pleasure to Maza's own five-year-old son.

"The boy can stay as long as he likes," Señor Maza had told Josefa. "Take him to the market and buy him smocks and pantaloons such as the other servants wear—and a *serape* for warmth. Much as José María admires the cape of grass, I doubt if it will last long in the city. Let Benito help you with the fires and other chores. When he learns a little Spanish, I will look out for a suitable master who will send him to school."

Through the rainy months of winter, Benito Juárez was well fed and warm for the first time in his life. The city was a continual enchantment to him. An enchantment and a challenge. The plaza, the market, the churches, the fiestas, the beautiful house of the Mazas . . . Even the chores were a source of pleasure. To cut wood for Josefa's stove, to scrub the tiled floors until they shone, to learn every day a few new words in Spanish, above all to live in an atmosphere of love and affection was like welcome rain to parched earth. And ahead of him was the promise of reading. He could wait a little longer. Patience was a characteristic of the Zapotecs—it was easy to be patient when you could see the goal ahead.

José María, young as he was, knew his letters. *Calle*, for instance the child explained, stood at the head of every crossroad. *Calle* meant street. Over the door of a certain stone building behind the cathedral was written another word Benito repeated to himself over and over until he learned its shape, its sound. *Escuela*. Benito learned that *escuela* meant school.

Josefa gave him a hug right on the street when he pointed out the word to her. "I declare, you are on the way to becoming a scholar!" she said.

"The doors are still closed to me," Benito reminded her. "How long, Josefa, until I am ready?"

Benito Juárez's chance came sooner than any of them expected. One evening, Señor Maza asked him into the dining room after dinner. There was a stranger at the table, an older man with a gray beard and a dusty black robe.

"Come here, Benito," the Señor said. "Padre Antonio wants to meet you. The padre is of the Order of St. Francis, a lay brother who lives and has his shop across from the Church of Santa Catharina."

The church of a hundred steps—to Benito's mind the most beautiful church in Oaxaca!

"Padre Antonio is a binder of books," Señor Maza

went on. "He has need of a boy to do his housework and help him in his bookbinding. I have told him about you."

Benito bowed his head gravely.

"So you want to be a scholar?" The padre's voice was low and musical. There was kindness in his dark eyes.

"I am Zapotec, Señor, I do not yet know many words in Spanish, but I will work for you day and night if only I can have schooling."

"The country needs Indian scholars," Antonio Salanueva did not ask if the boy could cook and take care of a house. His needs were few. "Tell your sister to pack your belongings. You can walk home with me tonight, if you wish."

Benito backed out of the dining room and ran across the patio. Josefa was sitting on the floor Indian fashion washing the dinner dishes. She couldn't trust the Mazas' fine china to the serving maid.

"What is it, Benito? You look—odd."

The boy swallowed hard. When his voice came back to him, it was high and squeaky with excitement.

"I have a place, with the padre. That little house across from the church with the steps. A man who makes books, Josefa. And the padre said 'home' as if I belonged to him—as if I were part of his family!"

"And school?" Josefa was a mother bird seeing her fledgling leave the nest. From the day he was born Benito, with his solemn face and eyes like coals, had been her child. She had left him because there was nothing else to do. The uncle had grudgingly offered her a home, but she did not feel welcome. Indeed, there was no room for her in the Guelatao hut.

"Of course, Josefa. The country needs Indian scholars. That's what the padre said."

The girl crossed herself and gave silent thanks to Benito's patron saint. Suddenly she became practical. "Your clothes are all washed. José María will be disappointed . . . Can we come to see you?"

"Of course. Don't worry, Josefa. I won't be far away."

3

A Book in His Hand

"Take this letter with you, my son. Present it to the schoolmaster." Antonio Salanueva held out a folded sheet of brown paper to Benito, but drew it back before the boy's fingers touched it. "Wait," the old man said. "I'll read it to you." His leathern face wrinkled in a smile. "Soon you will be able to read such words for yourself."

Benito Juárez was impatient to be on his way. Today was the starting point of his life. Everything that had come before—Guelatao, the flight down the mountain, the stay at the Maza mansion, even the two months in this little house of the padre—all that had come before was but preparation for living, a point of departure. But his impatience churned only inside his body. It was not in the little Indian's nature to show his emotions.

Slowly the bookbinder unfolded the scrap of paper left over from binding a book. He read:

Honored Señor:

This will bring to your notice Benito Juárez, Zapotec indio, aged 12 years, whom I have adopted as my godson. He is a bright boy and wishes to become a scholar in the Parish School.

Yours in the Faith,
Antonio Salanueva
Lay brother of the Order of St. Francis

Second day of March
The year of Our Lord 1819

A dream had become a reality. Benito bowed, tucked the letter in the pocket of his starched white smock, and stepped out into the spring sunlight.

The old woman next door was pouring water on her bougainvillea vine. With her free hand, she waved to him. She was mestizo and as a rule had no use for the Zapotecs from the mountains, but the padre's new boy was obliging and generous and had done several little favors for her.

"Out so early? Has the padre sent you to market? Where's your basket?"

Early? Benito had been up before daybreak, doing his chores. He could not restrain the smile that spread from his eyes to his wide mouth. "Today I go to school."

The old woman was not impressed. Her son had learned to read and write, she said, and what good had it done? As soon as he grew up he had joined the army of the unfortunate Morelos. If he was still alive, why did he not use his learning to write to his mother?

The smile did not leave Benito's face as he walked toward the big plaza—the *Zócalo,* Josefa called it. The rains were over. It was like walking in a garden. Every tree on the border of the sidewalk had burst into bloom. Jacaranda, magnolia, the casahute with its trumpet-shaped white flowers—Josefa had told him their names when they walked together during their free hour on Sunday afternoons.

The school was in the little building in back of the cathedral. The great bell was ringing for eight o'clock, but the bells no longer confused Benito Juárez. He walked boldly through the gates of the cathedral yard, felt for his letter, and entered the open door of the schoolhouse.

Classes were about to begin. Scholars sat at small desks, with books and sheets of white paper in front of them. Benito's darting eyes took in the books, the tablets, the quill pens on every desk. He moved toward the black-robed schoolmaster. A priest, of course. The Church had complete control of education.

The man read Antonio Salanueva's note and crumpled it carelessly on his desk. Without another glance at Benito, he pointed to the room in the back.

"You belong in there. The assistant will find a place for you. This room is for Creoles. I, myself, do not teach *indios*." That is left to the assistant.

The backroom was crowded with poor Indian boys. They had no desks in front of them, no books in their hands. They sat crowded together in rows on backless benches.

No one looked up when Benito entered. Their eyes were on the teacher as their fingers traced in the air the letters of the alphabet he called out. So this was the way the poor—the charity pupils—were taught to write!

"It is not just," Benito Juárez muttered angrily to himself. But when the writing lesson was over and he was motioned to a seat on the back bench, he directed all his attention to repeating after the teacher the words spelled in the air.

All that day and for days and weeks afterward, Benito concentrated on getting what learning he could from the miserable school. He said nothing of the conditions to Antonio Salanueva. The old man was doing the best he could to provide the education he had promised—and besides the padre, good and kind as he was, was nevertheless one of the foreigners. He was a Spaniard.

Benito Juárez never forgot the obstacles that were put in his path to getting an education. Fifty years later, when he had degrees in science and law and was elected president of the Mexican nation, he wrote down memories of his early schooling for his children:

> *The injustice* [he wrote] *offended me profoundly and so did the inequality with which instruction was dispensed. . . . I was disgusted with this wretched method of instruction and, since there was no other establishment in the city to which I could go, I decided definitely to leave school and to practice the little I had learned myself, so as to be able to express my ideas in writing, although the form might be poor, as it is still.*

Actually Juárez attended the parish school for about a year. Even during this time, he learned much more in the padre's house than he did in the classroom. Books were all over Salanueva's home—the padre's own books in his bedroom, books of prayers in the little parlor, books from the monastery to be mended or bound, and old manuscripts to be copied in the shop.

The subjects were almost all religious—the history of the Church, the lives of the saints—but that made no difference to the knowledge-hungry boy. As soon as he had learned the Spanish alphabet and solved the mystery of how the same thirty letters used over and over in endless combination created words, he read every book he got his hands on.

When Antonio Salanueva saw the earnestness with which his servant applied himself to learning, he began to direct the boy's studies. The old woman next door also took a part in Benito's education. She watched him reading while he carried water from the well, while he walked past her house on the way to do the padre's weekly marketing—from daylight to dark always with a book in his hand. One day she gave him a fat pine knot, rich in resin.

"Burn it," she said, "so you can have light to study after dark."

José María Maza brought a different kind of education into Benito Juárez's life. The little boy often came with Josefa to fetch Benito for the Sunday walks. As they strolled the streets or climbed the steep hill beyond the city—*El Cerro*, The Hill—where the guitar players gathered, José relayed conversations he had with his tutor. Words like "independence" and "liberty" and "constitution" became a living part of Benito's vocabulary. He got a confused but exciting glimpse of the events taking place outside Oaxaca.

The tutor who came daily to give José lessons had, it seemed, a brother fighting in the northern Sierras with the patriot Guerrero. The brother wrote letters that were much more exciting to hear about than anything in the padre's books. The tutor spent the whole day in the Maza household. He taught formal lessons, of course, but he taught much more than what was found in schoolbooks. Like Señor Maza, he was a man filled with the spirit of the revolution, with the spirit of liberty. And he was free to talk. Young José María was free to listen!

In the spring of 1821 José reported with assurance,

"When Guerrero comes out of hiding, the nation of Mexico will get independence. We Mexicans will have a flag of our own—not the royal flag of Spain."

Mexico? Mexicans? Benito Juarez knew the Spanish rulers and the Creoles, who looked like Spaniards but were born on Oaxacan soil. He knew Mestizos, like the woman who had given him the torch of resin to read by, and he knew the Indians, Mixtecs, and Zapotecs. Were all of them Mexicans? Would the foreigners go home? Would Zapotecs cease to be aliens in the land that was theirs? Would it be the future that Hidalgo and Morelos had fought for? José María said that Mexico was the name of an old Indian war god—a name that had come to stand for the whole vast Spanish-ruled land—but he could not give Benito all the answers. The seven-year-old boy was only repeating what he had been told by his tutor. Maybe nothing would happen, but the scraps of information brought to Benito's mind the memory of the days in Guelatao when he used to orate about liberty to his uncle's sheep.

Through the spring and summer of 1821, José María brought rumors of great events happening beyond the boundaries of Oaxaca, but the only thing that changed in the routine of Benito's days in the house of Antonio Salanueva was that he was set to copying a manuscript all alone. Day after day when the housework was done, he sat at the high desk in the shop with a quill pen in his hand.

Then one day in September an event occurred that made Benito almost burst with happiness. It was largely the padre's doing, but it was Señor Maza who broke the news to him. The *señora* was present—José María's mother—rocking the cradle of her newborn baby girl, Margarita.

"José María is going to enroll in a few years in the Royal Seminary," Señor Maza began.

Benito stood silent. It could not be to tell him of his son's future that the señor had summoned him from the padre's house. Naturally, when José's tutor had prepared him properly, Señor Maza's son would go to the Seminary with the other sons of the rich.

"My friend Antonio Salanueva tells me," Señor Maza continued, "that you have done so well in your studies that you are prepared to enter *now*. Would you like to go there?"

The Royal Seminary? The big building crowded with scholars of all ages in their robes—books in their arms? Not in his wildest dreams had Benito aspired to the Royal Seminary. Yet it was the only place in the state of Oaxaca where a real education was to be had. Benito Juárez looked down at his cotton pantaloons with his brown bare feet sticking out. He had never owned a pair of shoes in his life, had never thought of owning shoes or needing to. How could a penniless Indian, in the clothes servants wore, aspire to the Royal Seminary? Señor Maza must be joking. Still, though he was always gay and laughed a lot, Benito had never heard him make a joke at another's expense . . . "Are you serious, Señor?"

"Of course."

"Who wouldn't like to be enrolled in the Seminary! Does the padre really think I am a good enough scholar, Señor?"

"He has directed your reading all along with this in mind, Benito," the señora interrupted quietly. "But he did not raise your hopes, because of the money. When he mentioned it to my husband . . . It will be nice for José María when he is old enough to go to the Seminary to have you in the same school."

"Then it is all settled." Señor Maza dismissed Benito's stammered thanks with a wave of his hand. "Go tell Josefa that you will go. She has been bursting with the secret all week long."

4

Mexico Gets a Flag

In the same week that Señor Maza made his amazing offer to enroll Benito Juárez in the Royal Seminary of Oaxaca, the longed-for independence from Spain was proclaimed in the Mexican capital. But the separation from Spain did not come as a direct result of the struggle begun eleven years earlier by Hidalgo and Morelos.

Morelos' revolutionary movement, "beaten, broken, but stubborn" had gone underground, led by fugitive lieutenants of the great leader. The most important of these stubborn revolutionists was Vicente Guerrero. He operated between Oaxaca and Mexico City and was a name to be whispered with pride by Oaxaca Indians and by a few liberal intellectuals here and there. The staunch Guerrero remained a danger to the government of New Spain. He was declared an outlaw until the Church and the aristocracy decided to make use of him.

The change of government had been engineered by the enemies of liberty. The privileged classes in Mexico were determined to keep the way of life they had enjoyed in the colony. The powerful men of the Church, the army, the wealthy landowners felt threatened by events taking place in far off Spain.

The Spanish people, after a long period of fighting against the foreign rule of Napoleon, had their own king, Ferdinand VII, back with the condition that he rule under limited power. The French army was gone. The democratic ideas of the French Revolution stayed behind and had been adopted by the Spanish people in their Constitution of Cádiz. This constitution gave freedom of speech and thought to the people. It abolished the hated Inquisition. Ferdinand did not like the turn of events, but he had no choice but to accept the conditions. His Viceroy in New Spain was not pleased either. Yet he tried to publish the new, liberal rules of the constitution, and for this he was banished from Mexican soil, by his own colleagues and by the powerful Church rulers.

The independence proclaimed in Mexico City in 1821 was not the independence Indian patriots such as Hidalgo, Morelos and his lieutenant, Vicente Guerrero, had been fighting for.

The churchmen drew up a plan which they called the Three Guarantees of Liberty, and they devised a flag that symbolized the revolutions of Hidalgo and Morelos. The first guarantee called for unity of European- and Mexican-born people in the new government. (Nothing was said of the propertyless Indians who made up the vast majority of the population.) The second guarantee assured the Church that it would be the sole religious body and would retain all of its privileges. The third guarantee declared Mexican independence under a monarchy and promised that Ferdinand would be offered the crown as Emperor.

When Ferdinand VII refused to leave Spain, it was necessary to set up a local head of state. The Archbishop and a Dr. Monteagudo sent the head of their army, Augustín de Iturbide, to find Guerrero in his mountain hideout to offer the Indian revolutionary forces the opportunity to become part of the independence movement. Guerrero refused at first to deal with his old enemies but finally was tricked into a compromise.

Under the Three Guarantees, Guerrero agreed to march with his soldiers side by side with Iturbide's army into the capital of Mexico City. The man who had convicted Morelos of treason and heresy was the real head of government, with a Board of Governors of which Guerrero was not even a member. To prevent real freedom, Dr. Monteagudo and his followers had taken over the magic word "independence," and on September 21, 1821, pulled down the banner of Spain from the Royal Palace and ran up the new flag of the Empire of Mexico.

The flag was beautiful. It had the green of Hidalgo's banner and the red of Morelos' on a background of white. A constitution was not even mentioned. The Europeans in the Church circle, Mexican-born Spaniards, the Creoles and a few wealthy Mestizos came to power. The Indian population was ignored. Couriers were dispatched to the bishops of all the outlying provinces bearing news of the change of government. They went on horseback from one provincial capital to another carrying the new flag.

The news traveled slowly to Oaxaca. September had gone by and October was half over before the green, red, and white flag was raised above the palace which Cortés, the Spanish conqueror, had built for himself three hundred years earlier.

With hundreds of his fellow citizens, fifteen-year-old Benito Juárez crowded into the Zócalo to hear the bishop, from the steps of the cathedral, give his blessing to the new government. Bells rang and there was general rejoicing. The Royal Governor of Oaxaca was replaced by a Creole governor. Green plumes instead of the royal red appeared on the helmets of the palace guard. The name of Calle Isabella was changed to Calle Independencia, the Royal Seminary de Oaxaca became the Seminary de Santa Cruz. The structure, the make-up, of the society remained as it had been. The whites and near-whites of Spanish descent continued to hold all the offices; the dark-skinned barefoot Indians continued to live in back streets and take orders and do all the hard and unpleasant work.

Still, Mexico now called itself a nation. Independence had become a word you could speak out loud. For the first week or so, the sight of the Mexican flag waving over the palace portal and on El Cerro, the hill overlooking the city, gave Benito Juárez a feeling of elation. On the day he entered the Seminary, he began to have doubts.

The padre had filled Benito's arms with the proper books from his own library and triumphantly produced a scholar's robe borrowed from a Franciscan monk. The robe was old and patched and much too large. It covered the little Indian's white smock and pantaloons and swished about his ankles. Juárez was thankful that the good padre, who had sent him off with such pride, was not there to hear the jeers and laughter from the group of well-dressed scholars gathered at the Seminary steps.

It had not occurred to the boy that he would be the only Indian in the Seminary. The laughter of boys his own age hurt, but not as much as the contemptuous stares of the priests who were his instructors.

"Let them stare," he said to himself, and held his head high. He was no longer an alien. This was his country, his *Mexico*. Did not the first guarantee read by the bishop declare a union of all the inhabitants of the country? Was it so strange that a Zapotec desired an education? Zapotecs had lived in this valley and its embracing mountains for three thousand years.

"Without education, I cannot use my gifts, and gifts wasted turn bad."

At the end of the day, as he trudged alone to the house of Antonio Salanueva, he decided not to mention the coldness he had met with. There was so much that was good to talk about—the music lesson, the Latin. As for his classmates, "When they know me better, they will be more friendly," he said. If not, he could endure ridicule for the sake of an education.

All that first year, he had not one friend in the Seminary; yet he was not too unhappy. There was real learning to be had and his preparation was such that he could profit from it. Latin was his favorite subject. The exact logic of the grammar was something he could understand. And the violin he was taught to play was to give Benito Juárez pleasure to the end of his life. **1431088**

In addition to his studies, there were the household duties and the work in the padre's shop. Every moment was occupied. He had no time, and indeed no way, to find out what was going on in the nation. Yet every time he saw the flag, the question rose in his mind, "Is it really the flag of liberty?"

If there was talk at the Seminary of the unpopularity of General Augustín Iturbide, Benito did not hear it. He seldom had time for Sunday walks with Josefa and José María, from whom he might have heard rumors of rising discontent. So a very busy year passed in work and study before Benito Juárez heard the name of Vicente Guerrero spoken again.

Then suddenly in the autumn of 1822, the news drifted down to Oaxaca that the Empire had been brought to an end by a military revolt in Mexico City. Guerrero was the man who led the revolt, but it appeared that he had help from Augustín's own supporters. The Emperor had made the mistake of taxing the wealthy landowners.

Juárez was puzzled when he heard that the Emperor was banished. Who, then, was to rule the country? Would the Archbishop find another emperor? Would Guerrero have a place in the government? The priests at the Seminary seemed content to leave government in the hands of the Archbishop.

From the beginning Antonio Salanueva had hoped that his godson could become a priest. Independence for him simply meant that no more priests would come across the ocean from Spain. This would mean that the studious young Zapotec in his care would have a better chance to be accepted.

Benito felt no great interest in a life devoted to the rituals of religion. He agreed reluctantly to the padre's proposal that he prepare for the priesthood. It was not for a poor orphan to choose. There was nothing else he could do, since there was nowhere except the Seminary that he could get an education. Since childhood he had dreamed of independence and liberty. Independence had come, but the present reality was not like his dream. Was he right or wrong in his thinking? Never had Juárez needed a friend he could talk to more than at the moment when Miguel Méndez appeared at the Seminary de Santa Cruz.

Méndez was a Zapotec from Benito's own mountain region of Ixtlan. His father was a lawyer who had come down the mountain many years ago to work in a Spanish household as a servant. There was no law school in the province of Oaxaca, but somehow Señor Méndez had found a way to get legal training, and by the time Miguel was born had established a comfortable practice. A prosperous and able man, he had undertaken his son's education himself. The boy had tuberculosis of the hip and was not well enough to go to school.

Miguel Méndez was twenty when the doctors declared him well enough to attend classes at the Seminary. He still walked with a limp. The young man did not have the *double* handicap of being both an indio and poor. He was well-dressed, strikingly handsome, and at ease in any society. He had no difficulty in making friends.

Benito Juárez was attracted to the new scholar at once because he was Zapotec; but it was Méndez who made the first advances, who went out of his way to draw out the solitary, silent, but brilliant scholar. At first their talk was no more than the casual exchange of school gossip. It was not until a group of students decided to climb El Cerro one afternoon to hear a new guitar player that Miguel and Benito had any conversation alone.

Miguel fell behind the lively group of scholars as they began the climb to the hilltop. Juárez, more sensitive to Méndez's physical handicap than the others, slowed his own footsteps and soon the two young Indians found themselves alone on the trail. "They are in a great hurry to get to the top," Juárez commented.

Méndez laughed. "They're already on top in our world, aren't they—the foreigners, I mean." He used the Zapotec word for foreigners. It carried many meanings—conquerors, whites, all the long history of colonial oppression. "Especially," he added, "since the false independence."

Benito's dark, penetrating eyes opened wide with surprise. Could it be that this popular, successful scholar shared his own disappointment? "False independence," he repeated slowly. "That's a good name for what has happened. I've never heard it called that before. I thought—I thought that nobody else had doubts."

"Nobody?" Miguel laughed again, easily, comfortably, a joke shared between friends.

"The first day I saw our flag—the green and red stripes for Hidalgo and Morelos—I scarcely know what it was I expected . . ."

The floodgates were opened. Juárez's words tumbled over one another, in relief at finding someone to talk to. "Independence came and nothing is changed.

The first guarantee promised unity of all Mexican people. But the top is still on top and we, who belong to the land, are—nowhere."

Miguel Méndez paused on the path and, to rest his lame leg, leaned against the smooth trunk of a jacaranda tree.

"Let's sit down and talk a while, Benito Juárez, your thinking interests me. It's been easy for me to see that a real independence is still to be fought for. All I had to do was follow the lead of my father and his friends. But you've had to think the matter through alone."

"I am Zapotec," Juárez answered, as if that explained everything. "It seems only right that we should have some say in deciding about our lives, in arranging conditions. But always with consideration of others. Isn't that so?"

"The common people over the whole world believe as we do, Benito. The American Revolution, the French Revolution, even the Spanish people in their own country. Shall Mexico always be different? But fulfillment of the promise of democracy is like climbing El Cerro—not easy. Look at the country to the north, the United States. 'All men are created equal,' they say. Yet they enslave the blacks in large numbers. The French Revolution, with its cry of 'Liberty and Fraternity,' ended with the tyranny of Napoleon. And we? We have independence with the Three Guarantees, intended to keep the privileged forever in the saddle. Almost the only thing we have gained from Morelos' constitution is the abolition of slavery."

He pointed to the hilltop where the robes of the Seminary scholars were silhouetted against the sky. "Up there, they can look over the whole valley, the city, the farms, the mountains beyond. All theirs. But if they could see a wider view, the view of the future, they would not be so sure of themselves. New forces are gathering, Benito Juárez. The Emperor is gone. The Archbishop has invited a relative of Ferdinand of Spain to take the throne. But we won't allow a foreign king to reign over us. Mexico will be a Republic with Guerrero as President. People are ready to think, to speak, to act for themselves."

"You believe this, Miguel? I do not understand all you tell me. I only know that our flag is a symbol without reality. But if you believe it, then I do, too." Juárez no longer had to puzzle out great events by himself. He had found a friend.

5

Windows on the World

"When one has undertaken a social change, one must not halt until forces that oppose it are overcome."

The speaker paused and looked from one to the other of the company assembled at the home of Señor Méndez. He was a stranger to Oaxaca, having come down from Mexico City on this warm spring evening in 1827. To hear what the stranger had to say Méndez, the Zapotec lawyer, had invited fifteen or twenty men of the Liberal Party. Seated on the patio were several other lawyers in frock coats; Señor Antonio Maza and a monk in his cassock; a young guitar player, a friend of Miguel Méndez, in tight bright-blue trousers, open shirt, with a serape flung over one shoulder; and, on a corner bench almost hidden by a huge flowering geranium, a barefoot Indian in a servant's white smock—Benito Juárez. It was a group composed of different ages, different stations in life, united by their devotion to the new government, the Republic.

Almost all that Miguel Méndez had prophesied four years ago had come about.

The "false independence" was a thing of the past, and Mexico, since October 1824, was governed under a constitution. Vicente Guerrero had led the rebellion in the capital that brought all this about.

Delegates to a Constitutional Convention in Mexico City were chosen in various ways by the various states. At once they had entered into sharp debates between those liberal republicans who wanted a federal government patterned on the United State Constitution and the Conservative churchmen and landowners who clung to the second guarantee preserving the power of the Church. After many months the republican form of government was agreed upon, provided the privileges of the Church were left undisturbed. In 1824 the constitution was adopted and a temporary president agreed upon until elections could be held. The two parties, Liberal and Conservative, were busily organizing their forces for the election to take place in the fall.

Why, then, this sudden call to a meeting? What had brought the stranger all the way from Mexico City?

It was not the first time Juárez had been invited to the Méndez home when important discussions took place, but he was still a little overwhelmed at the new, unexpected world opened up to him. At the Seminary and at the home of the padre, the coming of a new government was scarcely noticed. At the Seminary, prayers were still offered for the banished Emperor, though Iturbide had been dead for a year. At Salanueva's shop, there was a little more work than usual because old books and manuscripts in the Church libraries had to be kept in good repair. No replacements would come from Spain. Neither at home nor in this distinguished gathering of republicans did Benito Juárez express his own opinions. Except when he was alone with Miguel, he generally listened in silence.

Although Miguel Méndez had long ago abandoned the Seminary, their friendship continued. When the young scholar was not well (and this happened more and more frequently), a note brought Juárez to his room. Together they explored Señor Méndez's library, overflowing with treasures Juárez would never see at the Seminary. It was here that he had spent a whole Sunday, after Mass, reading a copy of Morelos' constitution. Here, line by line, was the freedom Benito Juárez dreamed of . . .

The Constitution of 1824 fell far short of the dream. Even so, the document was too radical for the Conservative Party at the capital. Vicente Guerrero, old freedom fighter, head of the Liberal Party, and defender of the Constitution, was going to have a hard time getting himself elected to the office of president. As the speaker was saying, they could not—must not —halt until the opposition was overcome.

Juárez leaned forward to catch the next words of

the speaker. "We should have gone back to Morelos!" the man declared. "I know, I know, Señor Méndez, you and your Oaxacan delegation tried . . ."

"For months," Méndez answered, "but the army and the Church authorities, the Creoles, were too numerous in the Congress. The experiment in self-government was too young."

"Exactly." The stranger had the attention of the group once more. Juárez studied his long bony face with a nose like the corn-god's beak on Zapotec statues. An interesting man—a lawyer from his dress. Part Indian from his brown skin. Juárez had not caught his name. The important thing was that he had been introduced as a friend of Dr. Mora, a great name in Liberal Party circles. And he was staying as a guest in the home of Antonio Maza. But surely the professor from the university had not made the journey from Mexico City just to discuss the shortcomings of the Constitution!

"The first guarantee of unity with the Spanish element went out with the Emperor. Rising republican sentiment abolished the third. But the Conservative Creole landowners held to the second guarantee as if it were their lifeline."

"So it is," Benito Juárez whispered to Miguel.

"Our struggle for separation of Church and State cannot stop. Dr. Mora wanted me to remind you that as long as education is not free, the common people will have suffered and fought in vain and will derive none of the benefits they expected of the success of the revolution.

The speaker sat down to the sound of applause, led, Benito Juárez noticed, by his benefactor, Señor Maza. There was an air of expectancy in the group. So far nothing had been said that they had not said, many times, themselves.

Maza cleared his throat. "It seems to me, Señor, that the chief concern of the opposition is for their wealth. This is their meeting ground with the Church as an institution." He turned toward the tall man in the robe of a Dominican monk. "I mean no disrespect to religion, Dr. Aparicio. Morelos himself was a priest. But he knew and we know that to leave the education of our young men *solely* in the control of the Church limits their horizon. We must have windows on the world."

The monk gestured agreement. "We modeled our constitution on that of the republic to the north—the United States—but we omitted the foundation stone of freedom. I mean tolerance for every religion," he said quietly.

"Padre, we couldn't do everything at once." Señor Méndez defended the Congress where he had worked so long and so hard. "Without compromise we might not have a Republic today. At least the Conservatives accepted the abolition of slavery on Mexican soil. In that we are ahead of the United States whose Southern ports are still crowded with slave ships from Africa."

"Quite true," the stranger interrupted. "And if we break the hold on higher education, we go far toward undermining the second guarantee. Every college and university is still in the hands of the bishops. Frankly, that is what I want to talk to you about. Several of you gentlemen were sitting in the Oaxaca legislature last month. Tell me, is it not true that you quietly put through a bill for a civil college, separate from the Seminary? We, at the University of Mexico, heard rumors."

"The Oaxaca Institute of Science and the Arts."

Juárez smiled to hear the pride with which Señor Maza answered. Was a state-controlled institute really being planned? Perhaps this was why José María had delayed entering the Seminary.

"We passed a bill—true. But the Institute is still a dream—on paper." Señor Maza continued, "I do not think we would lack pupils. My son and several of his friends are ready to enroll. And there are scholars at the Seminary who long for the kind of education that will give more scope for their talents. But where, in Oaxaca, would we find professors with a knowledge of experimental science and modern languages? To say nothing of philosophy and the law and the arts?"

"Dr. Aparicio here is versed in Church law—a man of national reputation," the stranger persisted. "He is a churchman which would dispel any notion that you are setting up a rival to the Seminary. If Dr. Aparicio would consent to become director of the Oaxaca Institute, I would be happy to give the course in civil law. My friend Dr. Mora will find someone to teach philosophy of government. I confess that we talked this over before I left the University of Mexico. We consider that the action of your legislature has opened up a great opportunity."

"So, Oaxaca has something to give the nation!" A fat man with a beard and side whiskers folded his hands over his stomach and sighed with happiness. He was an Oaxaca lawyer, Tiburcio Cañas. "Dr. Cañesco, we are grateful to you for your offer," he said.

"Señor Canas speaks for us all," Juárez said to himself. *Law and the philosophy of government* . . . He could feel the rising enthusiasm.

Miguel Méndez volunteered to teach mathematics. "I will not be far ahead of my pupils," he said, "but what does it matter if we begin modestly? So long as we begin."

"My friend Bernardo Aloisi would be an excellent instructor in French," Señor Maza said. And then he proposed to donate his library—books by Voltaire, Rousseau, Condorcet, creators of the French Revolution. "And as for the building," he added, "there are the mansions of the Spanish grandees standing empty since their lordships followed the royal army to Spain." The vision of the Institute came like a rainbow to Juárez, in the colors of a rainbow over the Enchanted Lake of Guelatao.

"You'll tranfer from the Seminary, of course, Benito?" Miguel asked as he walked a little way with his friend after the others had gone home. "Civil law is just what you need."

"I would like to," Juárez answered slowly. "I am thoroughly bored with my course in theology. To go into politics, to speak for the poor people is my dream. But there is the padre to consider. Dr. Salanueva has his heart set on making me a priest. I cannot disappoint him. I cannot change schools without his permision, Miguel."

"You are of age. You can do as you please."

Juárez shook his head. "It would not be right."

To do right, to act justly, with consideration for the right of others, was the ruling passion of Benito Juárez's life. It is not by accident that today all over Mexico, on every wall painting and statue in his memory, his words are engraved: "Respect for the rights of others is peace."

The Oaxaca Institute of Science and the Arts opened in the winter of 1827. It took more than a year after that to convince Antonio Salanueva that it was best for his adopted son to leave the Seminary. Neither the fact that José María Maza was enrolled in the Institute nor the fact that the respected Dr. Aparicio was the school's director, nor that Dr. Cañesco and several other priests from the University of Mexico had come to teach there made any difference. The old man realized that more than a mere change of schools was involved. It was a great sacrifice for Dr. Salanueva. He would henceforth have to abandon all hope of seeing Benito Juárez ordained a priest. The young man's strength and endurance, his honesty and devotion would be given first to the nation rather than to the Church. What decided Antonio Salanueva to give in at last was the real love that existed between him and Benito Juárez.

"Go where God tells you," the old man said. "His ways are mysterious. Señor Maza tells me the Institute is the Seminary of the new world. The monk for whom I am binding the Epistles of Saint Paul calls it a house of the Devil. My faith in you tells me that you would do nothing that is evil. You have become a true scholar and brought honor to my little house. Pursue your studies where you will, my son."

Benito Juárez entered the Institute of Science and the Arts still a barefoot Indian, a servant in the clothes of a servant. Nevertheless, he was met with a warm welcome from the director and professors as well as from his classmates. He was escorted by Miguel Méndez from room to room in the massive buildings that had once been a palace.

The tapestries, the paintings, all the trappings of luxury were gone. Only the impressive stone stairway mounting to the balcony that overlooked the inner patio remained. Heavy doors opened from the balcony to the bare study rooms. The old ballroom had become the library; the dining hall, a science laboratory with delicate scales and test tubes and beakers of violet and green liquid that looked like the colors in the stained-glass windows of the cathedral. On the other side of the mansion were the lecture rooms of the Law School. Instead of Latin grammar, there were classes in living languages; instead of lectures on the super-natural world, the down-to-earth experiments leading to understanding of the laws of nature. And there were paints and canvas to recreate the beauty of the Mexican landscape. Courses were available in the natural law discovered by modern science, in civil law as a base for government, which dealt every day with the political questions as they arose in the Republic. Benito Juárez wanted it all! And he soon found himself taking part in political action as well.

The first presidential election since the adoption of the Constitution was going on. Vicente Guerrero, hero of the instructors and pupils alike, was the Liberal Party candidate and it seemed certain, if the voting was fair, that he would win. The political activity of the Institute enraged the Bishop of Oaxaca. He encouraged such attacks and slanders as Salanueva had hinted at when he reported that some were calling the Institute "a house of the Devil." Juárez had scarcely made himself at home in his studies when these accusations began to have an effect on the Institute.

Many parents withdrew their sons. By the winter of 1828 the attendance had dropped alarmingly. Juárez had been assigned to teach a beginning class in physics. With his first pay of thirty pesos he rented a little room near the Institute. He bought shoes and a properly fitting robe for his teaching, but as students were withdrawn from the new school he found himself with no pupils at all to instruct.

Students who remained in the school were cold-shouldered by their more religious friends. Young instructors, such as Juárez and Miguel Méndez, were attacked by hoodlums on the street.

A meeting was called to decide the best way to answer the accusations. Should they withdraw from political activity? Should they point out the number of priests on the faculty? Proclaim allegiance to the Church? Or should they simply bear the persecution in silence, hoping the Institute could weather the storm of abuse? The discussion was heated but seemed to arrive at no solution.

Juárez for once forgot his shyness, forgot that he had been an Indian servant. All his life an outcast, he now stood up to speak.

"The reactionaries say the students are encouraged here to voice their opinions on political questions and it is because of this that they persecute our director and professors. Of course we have political opinions. We are all liberals. We have the right to be. The clergy has a real reason to fear this new nursery of learning, where no bounds are placed on the search for truth. And truth—the truth about the nature of mind and matter discovered in science, the truth about the dignity and equality of man—will win. In time the power of the privileged few who hoard the wealth of the earth for themselves will be destroyed. The majority of human beings, ignorant and miserable, will find a voice. There is no turning away from the light of modern knowledge. Nor can we keep silent."

Juárez sat down a little embarrassed at the applause and cheers.

"What do you advise, Señor Juárez?" Dr. Aparicio asked. The young man's shyness was upon him again. The roomful of scholars waited for his answer.

"I do not know about rules of procedure. I am ignorant of many things," he said. "But it seems to me that if we trust the people, if we simply publish the notes of what was said here this afternoon, everyone of good will can see that we are acting in the best interests of the nation."

This was done. The prejudice and hatred died down. The institute survived and grew strong.

After the meeting Miguel Méndez was holding forth as usual to a group of scholars who clustered around him. Suddenly the fiery young orator pointed toward the corner where Benito Juárez again sat quietly listening, taking no part in the eloquent talk.

"This one whom you see here, so serious and reserved, will be a great politician. He will rise higher than any of us and he will be one of our great men and the glory of our country."

The prophecy of Miguel Méndez was long in being fulfilled and he did not live to witness its fulfillment. But it was remembered and repeated time and again by the young men gathered in that room.

⚭ 6 ⚭

The Curate of Loricha

The voting in the election of 1828 was over, but delay after delay took place in the Congress. Was Guerrero to be cheated of his victory? Were the people to be cheated of victory after long years of struggle?

In Oaxaca there was general rejoicing among professors and students alike when two armies began marching toward Mexico City to make sure that Guerrero would be installed as president. An old freedom fighter, Juan Álvarez, started out from Acapulco on the Pacific. Álvarez had fought under Morelos. His mother had been a Negro slave. When he led his men with the old cry of "independence and liberty," he spoke from the heart. The other troops from Veracruz on the Atlantic were led by a professional soldier, a wealthy Creole, Antonio López de Santa Anna.

Feeling ran high in the Institute when General Santa Anna, in plumes and gold epaulettes, entered Oaxaca shouting "Guerrero for President." The general had scarcely begun his recruiting campaign when news was brought from Mexico City that the Congress had given in to the threat of armed force. Guerrero had been named president of the Republic.

A professor at the Institute, carried away by the news, tendered Santa Anna a magnificent banquet. Among the honor students who were chosen to wait on the table was "the barefoot Indian" Benito Juárez. The two men whose names were to become linked in the history of their country for a quarter of a century thus came face to face.

"We have won with the wrong weapons," Juárez said soberly the next day. "No good will come of a victory that substitutes the threat of armed force for law. General Santa Anna was in the army that hunted down Padre Hidalgo. He will do the same to Guerrero if it suits his purpose."

No one, not even Miguel Méndez, agreed.

"Was it not right that Vicente Guerrero should be president?" Méndez argued. "If guns had to be used to make Congress count the ballots, well and good."

Two years later he had reason to remember Juárez's warning, when Vicente Guerrero was captured and executed in a field outside the city of Oaxaca. Santa Anna and his army had changed sides! In 1832, the year after Benito Juárez graduated from the Institute, Santa Anna was elected president of Mexico.

Neither Salanueva nor Miguel Méndez were present

to see Juárez receive his diplomas *summa cum laude* in philosophy and law. Old Antonio Salanueva had died in 1830 and Méndez, equally unaware of the defeat of the Liberal Party or of the honors that came to his friend, had recently died of typhus at the age of twenty-five.

"This one whom you see here . . . will be one of our great men and the glory of our country," Méndez had said. In the year immediately following Juárez's graduation, the prophecy seemed unlikely of fulfillment. The young Zapotec lawyer, dressed now in the conservative frock coat and stovepipe hat of his profession, opened a small office in the poorest part of town. Here even an unknown Indian might find a few paying clients and a multitude of charity cases. He lived in a rented room nearby and, except for the classes in physics he taught at the Institute and an occasional visit to Josefa at the Mazas, he saw only a stream of poor people in difficulties. With Santa Anna's Conservatives in power there seemed no future for a Liberal Party member in political office.

Then a curious bit of news drifted south from Mexico City. Without apparent reason, Santa Anna had retired to his country home in Jalapa. He left the government in the hands of his vice-president and defeated rival, Dr. Gomez Farías, a physician and the close friend of Dr. Mora, the philosopher. These two men introduced bills in the Congress of enormous importance to the cause of freedom. One bill put education in the hands of the state, another ordered Church lands that lay idle sold to landless farmers. "Education and liberty" once more became a popular slogan.

The Oaxacan Liberals took a deep breath and set out to elect a Liberal Party majority in the state legislature. Juárez was one of the successful candidates. His dream of serving in political office became a reality.

His first act as a lawmaker was to introduce a motion to honor the memory of the murdered Vicente Guerrero. That the motion passed unanimously caused no surprise; that Juárez was able to get the support of the army and Church for the ceremony he arranged was a tribute to his gift of persuasion, to the respect he had won in the city. A huge procession was led by the national guard in their plumed helmets, by black-robed priests and monks and nuns walking beside the soberly clad authorities in frock coats and stovepipe hats. Through the countryside, the whole Indian population followed. Guerrero, dark-skinned like his Indian mother, had been one of their own.

The hero's remains were lifted from the grave on the spot where he had been executed and carried in a silver urn to the convent where he had first been imprisoned. Bells tolled and muskets were solemnly fired. To Benito Juárez, who had conceived the plan, the ceremony was a symbol of the unity of the people for independence and liberty; but he was soon to learn that the army and the Church authorities were not ready to give up their privileges.

Shortly after the legislature adjourned, an old Zapotec farmer came, hat in hand, to his office door.

"I have heard there is justice for the poor in the Republic, Señor Juárez. I need help, but I cannot ask you to accept me as your client. I have no money to pay."

"That makes no difference," Juárez answered. "You have met with injustice? To serve justice is my purpose. Come in."

The man came a step or two over the threshold. He had walked, he said, the ten miles from the village of Loricha. "The injustice was not to myself, señor, but to another—to Pedro—a boy who, with my burro, is my sole help on my acre of land. Every year, you understand, I pay Don Manuel a certain number of bushels of beans. It is in the contract. But this year I could not. The drought, señor. It has never been so bad."

"Is this what you want to see me about? To ask your landlord to give you time until you can raise another crop? That should not be difficult." Juárez drew up a chair but the ragged, barefoot man remained standing.

"You do not know Don Manuel! Before half of the beans dried up in the field, he came to take my burro away. I do not complain. The contract gave him the right. But did he have the right, señor, to strike poor Pedro down because the boy clung, crying, to the beloved beast? The boy does not have all his wits—he could not understand about the contract. Now his leg is all twisted and I am afraid he will not walk again."

The case was plain to Juárez. No man has the right to injure another without punishment. How good it was that this man had the law to turn to! The landlord would have to answer in court. He would have to pay the crippled boy substantial damages. Everything in the Republic was not perfect, but the state at least could give protection to the poor.

"Tell me where to find this landlord. I can assure you, justice will be done."

"Don Manuel? At the convent, of course. He is the curate of Loricha, manager for the convent. Did I not say so? He collects rent for the nuns who own all the farmland in our village."

A curate? A man of the Church which had its own laws, its own courts. Benito Juárez sagged in his chair. How could he explain that the power of the Republic stopped at the door of the Church? For a civilian lawyer from the hated Institute to go before the Church court for justice to an Indian peasant . . .

And yet . . . Juárez wanted to be fair. Priests *had* walked in Guerrero's memorial. The Bishop even said a Requiem Mass in the cathedral. And in the nation, Dr. Farías, the Liberal physician, still sat in the president's chair . . . Things *were* better in Mexico. And the curate of Loricha had clearly committed a great wrong. To try this culprit in the Church court might not be as hopeless as it seemed.

Juárez turned to his waiting client. "Go back to your village," he said. "Do not worry. I will try to get justice for the boy."

It took courage for Benito Juárez to bring charges against a member of the priesthood, but he presented his petition to the black-robed judges as calmly as if he were explaining a physics experiment at the Institute. The petition was accepted and the curate of Loricha was ordered to appear in court in two weeks, to answer charges of cruelty and extortion.

Within these two weeks the whole climate of Mexican opinion underwent a change. General Santa Anna had suddenly returned from his ten months' retirement and reclaimed the power of the presidency. The liberal laws curbing the power of the Church were vetoed; Dr. Farías and his adviser, the noted Dr. Mora, were sent into exile. The wave of reaction had become a ripple by the time it reached Oaxaca, but it was still strong enough to relieve the curate of Loricha of embarrassment. Word came to Juárez that his client and Pedro, the boy, had been thrown into prison merely for making the complaint. When he hurried down to investigate, Juárez himself was arrested and charged with inciting the people against the authorities.

It has been said that those nine days in the Loricha jail completed the education which Miguel Méndez had begun. Certainly the experience made a deep impression on Juárez. To see injustice done and to be helpless to prevent it made it clear to Benito that the true independence of his country was not yet won. He realized that society could never be happy unless all classes of people were governed equally under one law. The incident of the curate of Loricha strengthened his determination "to work constantly for the destruction of the baneful power of the privileged classes." He was now a reformer for life.

All over the continent during the 1830's young men were making promises to themselves. Sometimes promises, long in coming true, are forgotten in the rush of making a living. Juárez did not forget. Nor did a lanky young raftsman in the North who had floated down the Ohio and the Mississippi rivers to New Orleans. In New Orleans, the young man read advertisements of slave traders offering "highest prices for Negroes." Offering "forty-five prime slaves—a very valuable young woman of 25, a good breeder." At the slave market the raftsman watched a girl auctioned off, first having been forced to trot up and down like a horse, to prove she had endurance.

"If I ever get a chance, I'll do something about slavery," Abraham Lincoln vowed to himself.

Both young men—Juárez and Lincoln—had a long time to wait, but both had endurance and patience and long memories. In the end, their lives as well as their goals came together, strangely entangled in a common struggle for freedom and the survival of their two countries. In Mexico, the law banning immunity from punishment for the military and for members of religious bodies bears Juárez's name. In the United States, Lincoln will be forever known for his signing of the Emancipation Proclamation, freeing Southern slaves during the Civil War. Both documents were cornerstones of liberty!

7

Margarita

Benito Juárez knew what he had to do for his country. He did not yet know how to go about it. He came back from jail depressed and weary. The old man and the lame boy were on his mind. And they were only two among the many poor and oppressed.

He did what he could and so did the Liberal Party. "Unfortunately for humanity," he wrote in his diary, "the remedy that was attempted at that time was not a radical cure for the evil, for although retrograde administrations were repeatedly overthrown and replaced by liberal ones, the changes were only of persons, while laws and constitutions continued to keep the immunities of churchmen and army. . . . The possession by the clergy of abundant wealth was used to encourage the causes that cemented their pernicious power. Thus it was that hardly a liberal administration was established than it was overthrown in a few months and its partisans were persecuted."

If this was true of Oaxaca, it was even truer in the rest of the vast country. Santa Anna's talents were military not political, and whatever he did was to satisfy his own greed and ambition. If a state revolted, his remedy was bullets. Liberals in 'the states of Zacatécas and Coahuila were killed off or exiled. When the revolt spread to the towns of the northern states of Texas settled by colonists from the United States, Santa Anna had a real war on his hands.

The huge, sparsely settled province to the north of the Rio Grande extended to the borders of the United States. Before independence, the Viceroy of Spain had given permission to North Americans to settle in the area, under Spanish rule, of course. The settlers were mostly from slaveholding states and they brought their slaves with them. They paid no attention to the Constitution of 1824, which abolished slavery throughout Mexico and looked to the United States for protection and trade.

The Liberals tried in 1830 to put a stop to immigration from the north, to put a stop to slavery. When Santa Anna and the Conservatives came to power, the Texans saw their opportunity and declared their independence from Mexico. Santa Anna marched his army north and brutally slaughtered the Texan garrison at the Alamo. This aroused the settlers to bitter defense. Under frontiersman Sam Houston, the Texans attacked and defeated Santa Anna's troops on the San Jacinto River. Santa Anna himself escaped, but was soon captured. To free himself, the general signed an agreement of independence for Texas.

The disaster showed the Mexicans how far they had to go before realizing the dreams of greatness, but the privileged classes remained in power. They did nothing to build the nation except to go into debt to France and England for money to carry on the government.

Oaxaca suffered with the rest of the country and Juárez took small joy in the fact that his own fortunes were rising. In 1841, at the age of thirty-five, he was made a judge, an office rarely accorded an Indian. Any pleasure he might have gotten from the honor was overshadowed by the thought that there was not just a single court of justice for the city but three. The army and the Church were still a law unto themselves. Neither military men nor priests nor nuns could be brought into civil courts for crimes. And there was less chance than ever to do anything about it, for after a few months of retirement, Santa Anna had been recalled to the capital. This time he ruled not as a constitutional president, but as a virtual dictator! Even after Santa Anna left for Cuba the Conservatives held the power in the capital.

The times were discouraging and besides, Benito Juárez was lonely. Since Miguel Méndez's death, he had not had a close friend. Josefa had married and moved to a village a day's journey away. He still went occasionally to the Mazas' home, partly from habit, but also he enjoyed the warmth of their family life. Señor and Señora Maza were getting old, but they had not lost their easy laughter and the house was always filled with music. José María had a fine singing voice and young Margarita played the piano. Often Juárez brought his violin. He was a family friend and did not need to question his welcome.

One night in the spring of 1842 he was brought to the realization that Margarita was no longer a child. A young man, a suitor, following the Oaxacan custom, walked back and forth, back and forth outside the parlor window. The young man it seemed had been "playing bear" night after night for weeks. It was a way of serenading, the Oaxacan way of proposing marriage.

"You are breaking Pedro's heart and wearing out his shoe leather besides," José María teased his sister. "You sent Carlos away—are you going to do the same with this suitor? Watch out or you will be an old maid."

"Your sister is not yet sixteen," his father said quietly. "You must not rush her into marriage, José."

Margarita blushed, but she made no move to show herself at the window. That would have been the signal that she was willing to accept José's young friend as a husband.

"How lovely she looks sitting at the piano. Such dignity and serenity and not yet sixteen." Benito Juárez felt a pang of jealousy. "Surely she has time enough to make up her own mind."

Juárez dropped in the next night and the next, relieved to see that Margarita kept away from the curtained window. On the third night the young man failed to appear.

"Pedro has given up." José María was disappointed, but Juárez's face broke into a smile.

"This is absurd," he said to himself on the way to his empty little house. "I am thirty-six years old and she is not yet sixteen. I must not think of love."

Absurd or not, on Margarita's sixteenth birthday a tramping began outside the Mazas' parlor window. Señor Maza took a look through a crack in the curtain and laughed. The sober judge, the family friend, was "playing bear."

"Why do you laugh, Papa? It's true, Señor Juárez is very homely, but he is very good," said Margarita.

"But he could have asked for your hand without going through this rigamarole!"

Antonio Maza studied his daughter. She was almost as tall as he—taller than Benito Juárez—so young and beautiful. Yet she knew goodness when she saw it. For Benito *was* good, steadfast and honest, both patient and wise. His daughter could do worse than marry the Indian. "Open the curtain and ask him in if you want to, Margarita," Antonio Maza said.

"You do it, Papa. Rap on the window with your walking stick." She had loved Benito Juárez for as long as she could remember.

The wedding took place the following spring. The Mazas gave Margarita a country house in the fashionable suburbs of Etla as part of her dowry. There, for a few months, Benito Juárez spent the happiest time of his life. When the court session opened, they came back to his plain little house in town. Except when they were cruelly separated by war, it never mattered to Margarita Maza where she lived. Where Benito was, there was her home. And in Margarita and their children, Benito Juárez centered his personal happiness.

Yet the measure of his faith in humanity, his determination to be of use to his country is seen in these years between 1836 and 1846. Neither the happiness he had won in his marriage nor the frustration of the futile, unsettled government weakened his determination to build a nation united under one law.

He studied continuously and wrote over and over again versions of the law to destroy, once and for all, the privileges, the immunities claimed by the wealthy.

In 1843 it seemed that the opportunity to act had come at last. Dr. Farías, who all these years had been in exile in Cuba, was again in the capital of Mexico. It is true that he had brought Santa Anna back with him from Cuba—the same mismatched team in the same official capacity—Santa Anna as president, Farías as vice-president. But Santa Anna was storming around the country raising an army and had again left the government to Gomez Farías. The Liberals in Oaxaca felt an upsurge of hope. Juárez was elected to the National Congress. He and Margarita and their two little daughters traveled by carriage to Mexico City and in their luggage went the many versions of the law Mexico needed.

Again disappointment met him. The hands of Dr. Farías were tied and the country was drifting helplessly toward war with the United States. It was clear to Juárez that this was a war for land, instigated by the powerful slaveholders on the border north of Texas, now a part of the United States. What he did not know until long after it was over was that Santa Anna, from the safety of Cuba, had urged President Polk in Washington, D.C., to march boldly into Texas and provoke the Mexican government to defend the territory it had never recognized as lost. The price for this treachery was to be ten million dollars—and its spending was to be in Santa Anna's hands.

"It is the only way," he had explained. "No government in Mexico City could stay in power a day if they simply *bargained* away hundreds of square miles of valuable land."

Santa Anna took command of the army. Farías was totally ignorant of the plot. He and his Congress only saw that they were in the middle of a struggle for survival.

"This is no time for pushing reforms," he told Juárez sorrowfully. "Your law for separating Church and State, mine for education, for the roads and harbors and industries we so greatly need—they all must wait for a happier day."

Juárez discussed the situation with Margarita. Was it worthwhile to stay in Mexico City where the Congress was powerless, where the mutinous soldiers paid by the clergy refused even to defend the capital?

"The news from Oaxaca is no better," his wife said slowly. "There, too, is rebellion. The legislature is dissolved, our friends persecuted. But there the name of Benito Juárez, doctor of law and professor of the Institute, has meaning. You may be helpful in re-establishing legal order."

"To work for the law," Benito Juárez agreed, "the law which has always been my sword and shield. Yes, it is in Oaxaca that my duty lies."

He had only one more job in the capital. Calling the three deputies from Oaxaca together, he proposed a resolution in the Congress condemning the mutinies of Oaxaca and refusing to recognize the authorities established outside the law. Armed with this paper from the general Congress, Benito Juárez and his family arrived in Oaxaca in August 1847. There was some fighting in the streets, but by November he and his liberal colleagues had succeeded in removing the usurpers from power. The legislature reconvened and appointed Juárez provisional governor of the state.

8

"You Know Our Needs"

October 29, 1847, was inauguration day of the new governor of Oaxaca. Down from Ixtlan and from Guelatao, to the trail's end, along the dusty outskirts of the city, past the market and the two-towered churches, a dozen Indians trudged to the Zócalo. At the door of the palace, they hesitated a moment, awed in spite of themselves by the festooned banners, the smartly dressed guards in striped trousers, bright coats and broad-brimmed hats. (The swords and plumed helmets, the marks of royalty and privilege, were gone.)

The lack of pomp was fitting. Benito Juárez was one of them. It was to see him sworn in as governor of the state of Oaxaca that they had come, bearing gifts. The moment of hesitation passed. In a body the barefoot Zapotecs moved toward the open door.

"Stop!" The captain of the guard stared at the white cotton smocks, the bright serapes, stared at the straw baskets carried on their heads filled with red and black beans, muscadine grapes, papayas and watermelons, and massive ears of corn. They had brought the best of their harvest.

"We have come to see Benito," the short, stout man explained politely in Spanish. Because he knew the language, he had made himself the spokesman. Three clucking hens raised their heads above the bed of straw in his basket. "Why do you stop us?" Felipe García spoke with assurance and dignity. "Is this not the *casa* of the governor? We have come to see Benito Juárez take office as head of our state."

"You are too late for the *Te Deum* in the cathedral," the Creole guardsman answered uncertainly. With an Indian in the governorship anything was possible. Perhaps these Zapotecs with their absurd baskets of groceries had been invited to the ceremony. "His lordship, the Bishop, has already administered the oath. Don't you understand me? You are too late."

"How could we come sooner?" García held his ground. "*You* try to cover the forty miles between here and Guelatao in less time than we took. We have walked the whole way in order to speak with Benito Juárez."

A hatless young man hurried across the wide corridor. It was José María Maza. "What is it, Captain?" he asked the guardsman. "Don Benito heard a commotion and sent me to ask the reason."

"These mountain men, Señor Maza. They claim admittance. Look at them! Do they look fit to attend a state reception?"

"We are from Guelatao, señor," Felipe García said.

"Guelatao? Benito Juárez would not want men from his village turned away."

The amazed captain of the guard saw the young man bow from the waist to this riffraff.

"All is as it should be," García said with satisfaction as he followed José María Maza through the door and up the majestic stairs. He remembered his cousin Benito only as a ragged shepherd, an orphan, a poor relative; but when the news came that an Indian and a Guelataon was elected governor, it seemed only right to pay him the honor of a visit. Felipe García had got together the delegation. Every person in the village had contributed to the gifts in the baskets.

They followed the young man in the velvet waistcoat into the brightly lit ballroom where Juárez and Margarita were receiving the greetings of their friends. Unabashed by the crowds that hid the governor from their sight for a moment, they stood by the door, listening to his high, clear, pleasant voice.

"Benito is making a speech," García explained to the others in the Zapotec language.

"Citizens will find in my administration the most solid guarantee of their rights," Benito Juárez was saying. "Free, and for me sacred, is the right to think and speak . . . That is good is it not? My compatriots will not be molested for their opinions in speech or writing. I shall respect them and I shall make them respected. But he who crosses the line drawn by the laws, he who violates the rights of others will suffer . . ."

The law—the law, always his shield and his sword. It was a pity that all the men from Guelatao could not understand what he said, a pity that the reason they could not understand the Spanish words was that Oaxaca still had no schools. The man standing before them, receiving the applause of the glittering assembly, would remedy that within a year—and the first village school he would authorize to be built would be in Guelatao, by the Enchanted Lake, where he was born.

The villagers waited quietly by the door, watching everything, saying nothing. They saw the beautiful señora in her lace *mantilla* and they recognized Josefa, dressed in silk, nearby. Josefa Juárez, who had run away from their village to become a cook!

At last it was the turn of his townsmen to greet Governor Juárez and to present their gifts. They spoke to him in the Zapotec language. "We come to see you, Benito, in the name of your village to tell you that we are very happy that you are governor. You know what we need and you will give it to us, because you are good and will not forget that you are one of us. Since we cannot bring you anything else, receive that which we bring in the name of all of us."

You know our needs. The common good, the well-being of all citizens would be Benito Juárez's object during all the years of his governorship—the needs of these friends not the least. What could he do at this moment to show his gratitude? Gravely, he gave each a peso as a token of deeds to come.

"I am a son of the people and I will not forget," he responded in Zapotec. He invited them to sleep that night in the palace, which they did, spreading their blankets on the floor in the corridor.

At dawn they set out again on foot to Guelatao.

In the five years that Benito Juárez served as governor of Oaxaca, he established more than two hundred free elementary schools and eight normal schools, where educated Indians could learn the art of teaching others. For the first time girls were given the opportunity to go to school because Juárez believed that they had a right to learning. He supported his cherished Institute with ample state funds and for a few months served as its director.

Juárez realized, however, that education meant little to a family whose children lacked enough to eat, whose parents struggled year after year under intense poverty because the crops they grew, the cloth they wove, the pottery they fired in their homemade kilns could not, for lack of roads, be brought to market. Therefore he built roads and bridges and had careful maps made of the city and the state. He even managed to build a harbor on the seashore where trading ships could dock.

He appointed trustworthy men, many of them his old pupils, to the civil courts. He was helpless, however, to improve the Church tribunals because the law giving immunity to the clergy stood like a wall in his way. He had not forgotten his vow to do something about this abuse of justice. The time had not yet come, however, when the rich and powerful in the Church and the army could be stripped of special privileges.

Juárez's efficiency and honesty and hard work became an example to the whole country. To save money for schools and roads, he stopped the wasteful show of former governors and did not even make his home in the palace. With his large and growing family, he lived in an old house about a block beyond the cathedral.

"Every morning, when the bells of the cathedral sounded at nine o'clock," Madame Calderón de la Barca, the wife of a Spanish diplomat, wrote in her journal, "Juárez appeared in his somber citizen's suit on the way to his office, so that the astonished aristocrats remarked that the governor might as well be a common workman."

Workman he was, for the good of all the people— this in a time when the rest of the country was in the kind of chaos that follows defeat in war. Soldiers of the invading army of the United States still occupied forts surrounding the capital. The diplomats from the north forced the president, José Joaquín Herrera, to sign away over half the Mexican territory as far west as the Pacific Ocean, as far north as the present state of Missouri, as the price of peace. The fifteen million dollars the United States finally paid for indemnity went for interest on the foreign debts. The cost of running the national government had to be borne by contributions from the states. Under Juárez, Oaxaca made the largest contribution by far.

"A single state, Oaxaca, has shown itself firm, consistent and even heroic," Ramirez, a noted newspaperman, wrote at this time. "It has provided everything, money and men, amid its own trouble."

"Everything" did not prove enough to save Mexico from dismemberment. Santa Anna had been dismissed from the army of the Republic and was roaming the highways and byways, looking, as usual, for trouble. The defeated general still had a following in Oaxaca among those whose power was threatened by Juárez's government. When they heard that Santa Anna was on the border of the state, these eternal rebels sent messengers urging him to enter the city.

On the other hand, the city council and the state legislature appealed to Juárez to prevent the entrance of the "troublemaker." Juárez sent word to the border town of Teotitlán that it would be harmful to public order for Santa Anna to come any closer to the city of Oaxaca.

Santa Anna withdrew, disgruntled, and soon afterward left for Venezuela. The murmurs against Juárez's government quieted down and he went on serenely with his work. Santa Anna, however, took Juárez's order as a personal insult. "The Indian hates me," he said, "because he waited on me at table in Oaxaca in 1829, with bare feet on the floor and in his linen smock," Santa Anna said bitterly to anyone who would listen. "It is amazing that an Indian of such low degree should be a figure of importance in Mexico!"

Benito Juárez had made a dangerous enemy.

9

Santa Anna's Revenge

Juarez's elected term as governor came to an end in the fall of 1852. He retired, feeling that he was leaving the affairs of the state in good hands. The new governor, Ignacio Mejía, had been his student at the Institute. He was a capable man and could be trusted to continue to build on the foundation Juárez had laid.

Governor Mejía's first act was to appoint Benito Juárez director of the Institute of Science and the Arts. The salary was only five hundred pesos a year, but Margarita's mother had died during Juárez's term as governor, leaving them a fortune ample enough for their frugal needs. And they had the lovely Etla house to live in. Money was not a problem at this time.

If Mexico had not been a country uprooted from its fruitless past, uncertain in its future, Benito Juárez would have settled down for life as a part-time scholar and a gentleman farmer. But the Republic was a structure whose very foundations were still uncompleted. The land was not owned by the people who cultivated it; those with the power to hurt still lived outside the law, still considered themselves above the Constitution. They were never content and were always plotting rebellion. When reactionaries in one state saw a path to power, reactionaries in other states were quick to follow. The clergy supported the army officers; the army fought the battles of the Church. Between them, they prevented any legally elected national government from staying long in power.

In January 1853, General Pinollos of Oaxaca was sent to put down a small rebellion in the state of Jalisco. Instead, he joined the spreading rebellion. Santa Anna, the ever-ready, was recalled again to power in the national capital. Ambitious men in Oaxaca came forward to reap the rewards. Juárez's life was threatened and he was dismissed from the Institute. Governor Mejía was also forced out of office. There was nothing that could be done for the moment except to wait patiently until the storm of reaction spent.itself.

"Don't worry, this will pass," Juárez said to his wife. "We will live happily in Etla until we can be useful to the people again."

Etla! Rolling hills, orchards, flower gardens, a meadow knee deep in grass where the children's ponies could graze . . . Beauty and leisure were theirs for the first time since their marriage. Juárez had time to enjoy the growing girls, to hear their lessons, to listen to them practice the piano, time to give lessons to young Benito and to answer the questions of Pepe, his remarkable five-year-old son. All the affection, all the family fun, all the security he had been deprived of in childhood, he gave to his children.

The winter and spring of 1853 was a kind of golden holiday for the "little Indian" and his understanding and devoted wife. (The "little Indian" was what the people called him and they said the words out of love and admiration.) He was forty-seven years old, Margarita not yet thirty, but it amused him to call her his "old lady." She seemed to him so young and yet, surrounded by her many children, so dignified and womanly. They looked forward that spring to a long, quiet life in the country.

Juárez still had his law practice among the poor people—his own people in nearby villages; except for occasional court appearances, he seldom left Etla. But on May 14, he saddled his horse for a longer journey than usual. He had to appear for a client at Ixtlan, on the mountain near Guelatao. He would probably stop by his old home, he said, to see how affairs in the village were progressing. Then, on the way home, would go to the village of Teococulco to take the testimony of a witness since Teococulco was no distance from Etla. He should, he said, be home for dinner and a romp with the children on the seventeenth or eighteenth at the latest.

He had reckoned without Santa Anna the dictator in Mexico City. At Teococulco, Juárez was interrupted in his talk with the witness by the clatter of armed troops sent by Santa Anna to arrest him. He was charged with having incited the people in the region against the authorities. There was no trial. He was escorted, a prisoner, through Etla, where he begged to be allowed to say good-bye to his family. Brusquely, the captain of the troop refused. His orders were to pick up two more prisoners in the city of Oaxaca and to escort the three "enemies of the nation" across the border of Oaxaca. After that they would learn his Excellency's plans.

All over the country, Santa Anna was rounding up Liberal Party leaders who might become a danger to his dictatorship. No one had any warning. The local people were bewildered and helpless as they watched Benito Juárez herded through Oaxaca.

The guard changed at the border. Juárez's condition as prisoner did *not*. On the second day he found himself in jail in the fortress of Puebla; on the twelfth of June at Jalapa, in Santa Anna's own state of Veracruz. From here, he and Felix Romero and another stranger were shunted from one jail to another.

On September 19, José de Santa Anna, the dictator's son, suddenly appeared and took charge of Juárez and conducted him to the coast outside the city of Veracruz. Here, for the first time, Benito

Juárez saw the turbulent waters of the Gulf, heard the roar of the breakers. Next day he was taken by boat to the Castle of San Juan de Ulloa, on a barren little island. Here he was thrown, still unable to communicate with his wife, into a dungeon, below sea level.

"I remained incommunicado in the castle," he recalls in his memoirs, "until the 9th of October, when at eleven in the morning, the governor of the castle informed me of the order for my exile in Europe and handed me the necessary passports. By this time I was ill and I answered the Governor that I should comply with the order as soon as I was better. But he was inexorable and told me that he had an order to make me embark on the English packet *Avon*, which was due to leave the port at two o'clock in the afternoon of the same day. Without waiting for any reply, he himself seized me and took me to the ship. Only at that time there came to an end my solitary confinement. . . ."

All this while Margarita had had no word from her husband, but somehow the rumor that Juárez was in the Veracruz dungeon reached her. She was frantic. She managed to mortgage the Etla house for 400 pesos. (The peso was worth about the same as a dollar at that time.) Unable to leave her children, she sent her brother, José María, to Veracruz with the money. When José arrived at the castle, the prisoner was already at sea.

On board the *Avon*, Juárez was equally anxious.

On the docks, as he was marched to the ship, he had heard that yellow fever was raging in Oaxaca. Only three years before, during an epidemic of the sickness, lovely little Guadalupe, his daughter, had died. He had carried her coffin in his own arms to the city graveyard. Now if the sickness struck, they would have no father to care for them. To be across the immense, pounding waters of the Atlantic from his family was like being dead . . . Somehow he persuaded the ship's captain to disobey the orders and to let him disembark in Cuba. He spent the last day aboard ship writing letters home.

When he landed at Havana, he found another exile, the distinguished young scholar José María Mata. Mata had not come down to meet Juárez, had barely heard of him as governor of the state of Oaxaca; but they were both exiles, both the victims of Santa Anna. In an hour, the two became good friends. Mata explained that he met every incoming ship because he expected Don Melchor Ocampo, former governor of Michoacán, and the daughter who was sharing Ocampo's exile. "The Señorita Josefa Ocampo is the young lady with whom I am in love," Mata confessed without shyness. "For me, exile in the company of the Señorita and her father will not be a hardship. We are going to the United States, to New Orleans. Havana is not a safe place for enemies of Santa Anna. Already many of our exiled compatriots are gathered at New Orleans. You must come, too, Don Benito."

"To New Orleans?" Exile with a man like Melchor Ocampo would lose half its sting. Juárez had heard only good things about the great scientist and of his botanical experiments. He had read in the law journals of his defense of a poor Indian against the abuse of a parish priest—it was a case similar to his own against the curate of Loricha, but a defense expressed in eloquent language. He looked forward eagerly to meeting Señor Ocampo. But to go with them to New Orleans was out of the question. Where would he get money to pay his passage? He had exactly ten pesos which a sympathetic passenger on the *Avon* had pressed into his hand as he came down the gangplank.

Juárez made some noncommittal answer to Señor Mata, but he was with him next day when a ship was supposed to come in from Veracruz. Ocampo, handsome, articulate, a world traveler, came down the gangplank with his daughter. He was not surprised that Mata and the Oaxacan had found each other in Havana. He, too, had been in the Castle of San Juan de Ulloa, but had not been able to make contact with Juárez in prison.

"I knew, Don Benito, that you had been transported, but we thought your passport was for England. Your brother-in-law and I were much concerned for you."

"My brother-in-law? José María Maza?"

"He is aboard this ship, but he could not come ashore—he left Veracruz so hurriedly that he has no visa for Cuba and cannot step on land."

"José is here?" Juárez could not believe it. "Does he bring bad news? My wife? My children? I heard there is yellow fever in Oaxaca . . ."

"Wait," Ocampo said, smiling. He ran back up the gangplank and in a few minutes returned with José María—his visa had been arranged.

José had to assure Juárez half a dozen times that his family were safe and well. "Margarita's only anxiety was about *you*," he said affectionately. "She hustled me off with money for you as soon as news came that you were in that black hole in Veracruz."

The invitation to join Ocampo and the other exiles in New Orleans was repeated. Juárez knew that there was not enough money for first-class passage for himself and José. Ocampo was a wealthy man. He would have offered to pay. This, Juárez didn't want. He made the excuse of waiting a week in Havana for mail and promised to come by the next boat.

Maza and Juárez worked for their passage as ordinary sailors. It was as well they did, for the four hundred pesos José had brought was the last money they saw for many months. The letter Juárez waited for in Havana brought the news that Pinollos had seized their home in Etla, and all the property Margarita had inherited as her dowry. Margarita was opening a little shop in the village and would live above it with the children. "You are not to worry about us, my dear husband," she wrote cheerfully. "We are among friends and will take care of ourselves until you can return."

Don Antonio López de Santa Anna in his palace in Mexico City had done his best to destroy the young, just-rising democracy in his country. Actually, in banishing his enemies, he made possible the fulfillment of all their dreams. The exiles, brought together in the shabby little boardinghouse in a foreign country, became the future builders of an independent self-governing Mexico. Ocampo; Mata; Poinciano Arriaga; Juan Batista; Ceballos, the first appointed president, in 1824; Captain Perraza, from Yucatán; Santacilla of Cuba—and Benito Juárez of Oaxaca. This was the core of the group whom Santa Anna unwittingly brought together. At home, they had been lonely believers in freedom, isolated from each other, each in his own state. In exile, they discovered a new strength in one another, in the common task they set themselves, which was nothing less than revolution.

❧ 10 ❧

The Return of an Exile

The day after Juárez came to New Orleans, a meeting of the exiles was called in the room of Melchor Ocampo to consider the best way to overthrow Santa Anna. To the people of New Orleans, they were nobodies—a group of shabby, penniless foreigners. Benito Juárez had come to a city where black slaves were regularly sold on the auction block, where any dark-skinned person was suspect.

At home, although most of them could point to some accomplishment and a small following in their own separate states, only Ocampo had a national reputation. He had been a man of some wealth, but he had no sooner reached New Orleans than he heard that all his land, his home and his beautiful gardens had been confiscated; the famous botanical books he had written were banished from the libraries. Señor Ceballos had, for a brief time, held the title of President of the Republic. Arriaga, of San Luis Potosí, had been arrested for "spreading dangerous ideas" in his political pamphlets. Perraza and Mata had been driven out simply because they were known to belong to the Liberal Party, Santacilla, a foreigner, because he associated with the Liberals. The conspirators were men of no great prominence, but they shared a vision and a faith in the future. And none of them questioned that their future lay in Mexico, the country that held their hearts.

By day they worked at whatever miserable jobs they could find. Ocampo, who had a good suit of clothes, worked as a waiter. Arriaga made friends with a Mexican who had a small print shop. Rafael Cabañas, the printer, taught the young aristocrat to set type and also printed the revolutionary manifestos Arriaga wrote for the conspirators. Juárez and Maza rolled cigars to sell at night on the busy streets. When they had made enough money for supper, they stopped at the food stalls on Market Street and ate tasty Creole *gumbo* or fried plantains or watermelon, standing up. Often there was only money enough for a slice of black bread. And the evenings were cut short by the curfew, when no Negroes—and this included anyone with a dark skin—could walk on the streets without a pass. In the late hours of the night, they worked on the Plan the exiles wanted to perfect—a plan for Mexican liberation from tyranny.

One red-letter day that winter a former Collector of the Port of Acapulco, Señor Ignacio Comonfort, was brought to their meeting. Comonfort had escaped arrest in Santa Anna's round-up of Liberals. He was not an exile, not poverty-stricken, but he shared the conspirators' aspirations for a better society for Mexico. He was on his way to New York, at the request of Juan Álvarez, governor of the state of Guerrero, to buy guns for a rebellion.

Álvarez was a magic name to Benito Juárez. Long ago Méndez had named him as a freedom fighter under Morelos. His name had appeared again in the days of Vicente Guerrero. Álvarez, whose mother had been a slave from Africa! And now, Señor Comonfort, the old hero's friend and adviser, was sitting here in this room!

Furthermore, he brought with him a plan of government prepared by someone in Ayulta, a plan that Álvarez would proclaim as a goal for his uprising against Santa Anna. Anxiously the plan was examined. It was limited in scope, meager in ideas; but it would serve as a beginning. Melchor Ocampo asked if they could keep it, improve on it and send it to Comonfort. They would have it in Acapulco by the time Comonfort's journey to New York was completed.

The new Plan of Ayulta, when it was finished, kept its name, but otherwise bore small resemblance to the original. The noble ideas of Jefferson and Tom Paine; the passionate love of humanity expressed by the French Revolutionary writers and the Bill of Rights; Ocampo's deep concern for "the complete man;"

Juárez's rule of law, one law for all classes of people without special privilege for some—all the radical reforms on which a democratic nation could rise—all this was implied or expressed in the new Plan of Ayulta, sent by courier from New Orleans.

Certain ideas were too strong for Comonfort and he softened the language, but there was enough left when Juan Álvarez proclaimed it to start a blaze in the country, a blaze of freedom!

Rebellion began in Acapulco in the state of Guerrero but spread almost at once to other areas. Santa Anna had 95,000 soldiers and he sent armies to one spot and another, but he could not stop the fires of revolt. Months passed before news came to the exiles in New Orleans. The winter had gone by and the spring had given way to broiling summer weather. The hotel, cheap as it was, had become too expensive for Juárez. He and José Maza moved into a bare attic which a Negro woman let them have for eight dollars a month. She fed them both for eight dollars more.

Juárez urged José to go home to watch over the family. Before his brother-in-law could get passage on a ship, Juárez was stricken with yellow fever. For weeks he lay helpless. José Maza slept on the floor beside him and Ocampo moved into rooms in the house to be near. Juárez's will to live was stronger than the death that threatened. He recovered his health and, made both happy and anxious by letters from Margarita, finally persuaded José to return to Oaxaca.

By November 1854 rebellion had broken out in Ocampo's own state of Michoacán, led by his friend, the scholar Degollado. Liberals were rising in Guadalajara in the state of Jalisco. Ocampo and Arriaga moved to Brownsville, Texas, near the border, to try to waken the northern states in Mexico to action. But Juárez put his faith in rough old Álvarez, moving under the Ayulta battle cry of "Justice, Liberty, and Equality."

In March 1855 he and the other conspirators remaining in New Orleans, sent a letter to Ocampo urging him to go to Acapulco, saying, "Your presence will raise the spirits of the public."

It was not enough, Juárez thought, to rise up to drive out Santa Anna. The Plan, their plan for thorough revolutionary reform, must be made the goal. Without the presence of the exiles this would not happen. Ocampo replied that he was ill but would cross into Mexico with Arriaga and Mata as soon as he was able. Juárez wrote again urging a reunion of all the conspirators in Acapulco. He would start out as soon as money he was expecting from home made the journey possible.

The money did not come; but in June a letter from the Brownsville group appointed Juárez the representative of the revolutionaries. Two hundred fifty pesos were enclosed to pay for the long trip.

Juárez left immediately by ship for Havana. Another ship to the Isthmus of Panama, then across the narrow neck of the Isthmus by rail. On the shores of the Pacific, he caught a freighter carrying coal. There was not enough money for passage. In his travels he had lost his portmanteau containing his good frock coat and precious books. So in travel-stained jacket and trousers, he signed on as a sailor and was set to loading coal in the hold. The freighter *Flor de Santiago* was bound for San Francisco, with stops on the way in Costa Rica, Nicaragua, Honduras, El Salvador, Guatemala, and, at last, Acapulco—a long, hard voyage. It did not matter. His exile was over. He was going home to Margarita and the children, home to fight for justice, liberty, and equality on Mexican soil!

For two years Benito Juárez had been away from his family, his work, and his country, but the years had not been wasted. He had strengthened and crystallized his dream of making a better society. He had come to New Orleans the least known, the least considered of the exiles. He had been only a provincial governor and an Indian. He was returning as the acknowledged representative of some of the greatest men in Mexican history. His mind was enriched, his endurance tested by adversity.

Juárez left the ship penniless, in a ragged coat, his white shirt, always so spotless, now tattered and streaked with coal dust. To those he spoke to on the waterfront, to ask the way to General Álvarez's army, he appeared just an aging Indian sailor.

"The army? It's off fighting, of course. Here we have peace and victory. Acapulco is free. We don't have to listen to the sound of guns."

"It's Álvarez I'm looking for," Juárez persisted.

A woman selling tortillas from the basket on her head pointed. "Over there, on the second street is the Álvarez house. You can try there."

General Álvarez's house was built of adobe. A wide door stood open on the street. What may formerly have been a patio appeared now to be an office. A hot July sun beat down from a skylight onto the shoulders of a black-haired young man seated at a desk. His chair was tipped back, his feet, in polished army boots, hoisted up on the desk top.

Juárez advanced only a few steps into the room.

"What do you want?" The voice of the young man was flat and unconcerned. He might have been talking to a beggar.

Juárez suddenly realized what a shabby figure he cut in the young man's eyes. *The representative of the men of the Plan of Ayulta!* He did not know how to begin.

"I am looking for General Álvarez," he answered slowly. "Knowing that men are fighting for freedom here, I came to see in what way I could help."

"I am the general's son. How old are you? You look to me too old to do much fighting. Besides, now that the other states are rising and victory is certain, my father has no lack of recruits. They tumble from every little shack, like fruit from a tree."

So the good news was true! Young Diego Álvarez had said that victory was certain . . . Juárez forgot his inborn shyness long enough to ask, "What of Oaxaca? Is Oaxaca in rebellion, señor?"

"I believe so." Don Diego's feet came down on the floor. He began to show some interest. "You are Oaxacan? Can you read and write? I hear even the poor there can go to school."

"I can read and write," the man who had built the Oaxaca schools answered, without further explanation.

Don Diego looked at him dubiously. His father needed a secretary. With victories piling up, letters poured in for General Álvarez. A dozen were on the desk waiting delivery to the encampment. A volunteer with education could make himself useful.

"I am riding out to camp in a few minutes. You can come along, on one of the pack horses. You can ride horseback, I suppose?"

Juárez nodded.

Don Diego reached under the desk and came up with a pair of old boots. "Try these on," he said. "It's the rainy season. In those sandals you're wearing, you will sink ankle deep in the mud."

No other words were spoken until a few hours later, when Benito Juárez followed the young man into the hut that served General Álvarez as headquarters.

"I brought you a secretary," Don Diego said to his father with a little laugh. "He said he wants to help fight for liberty."

They had ridden through a tropical storm. The rain had finished off Juárez's tattered jacket. His coal-streaked shirt showed through the jagged holes. Drenched and shivering, he nevertheless joined in the general's laughter.

"A secretary? He looks more like a scarecrow in urgent need of repair." Álvarez lunged for the cot behind him and jerked off the woolen serape that served as a blanket. "Take off that wet coat and put this around you."

He clapped loudly and an orderly appeared, a Negro in the familiar white cottons of the Mexican workers. (Álvarez spent his money on ammunition, not uniforms.)

"Find a shirt and trousers to fit this newcomer."

The blanket felt good and the cotton trousers and shirt, when they came, were only a little too small. Juárez was reminded of the hand-me-down scholar's gown he had been forced to wear in the days of the Seminary. At least this present makeshift would not trip him up. The trousers hardly came below his knees.

"You say you can write? In good Spanish?" General Álvarez himself had had little opportunity for education. The son of a slave in New Spain in the early days of the century, he never saw the inside of a school. He began to dictate a letter to Comonfort and with awe watched Juárez set down the first words.

Benito Juárez wrote in the beautiful flowing hand he had been taught by the Padre Antonio Salanueva. He could write Spanish, Zapotec, French, Latin, Italian, and (since New Orleans) a little English. But General Álvarez's correspondence made no great demands on his knowledge. The letters were chiefly demands for further supplies. But Álvarez always closed with a flourish, "Yours for justice, liberty, and equality" . . . the words of the Plan, their own Plan of Ayulta!

Álvarez called his secretary "Benito."

It was not until a week or so later when Santa Anna had retreated to Veracruz and was preparing to leave the country that Juárez's identity became known. A letter from Melchor Ocampo was delivered to headquarters, addressed to "The Honorable Doctor of Laws, Benito Juárez."

"Why the devil does Señor Ocampo write to his distinguished friend here?" General Álvarez fingered the stiff, white envelope. "I think the letter is for me, General," Juárez said without embarrassment.

"You are Benito Juárez, Doctor of Laws and former governor of Oaxaca?" Álvarez shouted. "Why the devil didn't you say so?"

"I came to help and you gave me work I could do. Why should I say who I once was? Of what importance is that?"

❧ 11 ❧

"Ley Juárez"

On August 17, 1855, Santa Anna gave up and retired
to Havana. The Plan of Ayulta was proclaimed triumphant in the capital. The proclamation was issued
by the Church authorities and by a group of generals
who had fought under Santa Anna, but its goals of
civil freedom were not meant to be taken seriously.
This military *junta* in the name of "justice, liberty,
and equality" proceeded to name General Martín
Carrera, one of their own men, as president of the
Republic.

The news that the dictatorship was at an end swept
the country. Word reached General Álvarez and his
secretary in the city of Acapulco where he had come
in from the field to transact some business. Church
bells rang and there was general rejoicing. Peace, victory, and the Plan of Ayulta . . . What more could
one ask?

There seemed nothing to do but applaud the event.

Juárez was instructed to give a copy of the Plan and a congratulatory statement in Álvarez's name to the newspaper. The manner of the victory troubled Juárez, but he did as he was told. However, he knew that whole thing was a trick to destroy the revolution in its infancy. As the chosen representative of the exiles he felt it his duty to speak, before Álvarez's statement came out.

At supper that evening he brought up his doubts of the "victory." "Does it not seem to you, General, that the revolt in Mexico City might be simply to save the skins of the generals now that Santa Anna is gone? They are stealing the fruits of patriots like yourself from under the noses of the true revolutionaries, who flung themselves into the fight to free the country from clerical-military tyranny."

"You are right!" Álvarez banged on the table. "We have nothing in common, you and I, with those followers of Santa Anna. I wondered when I heard the church bells ringing. They have never rung for a people's victory before."

"The facts are clear," Juárez answered quietly. "But nobody seems to have taken the trouble to examine them."

"*You* have, Benito. Write out what you have told me. Go down to the newspaper and stop the printing of my statement until you have corrected it. For myself, I am a soldier. I will ride to my headquarters tonight and prepare my army to march on the capital to establish the kind of government we have been fighting for. When the paper comes out tomorrow morning, send a copy to Señor Comonfort in Guadalajara. Tell him to join us on the road as quickly as he can. Comonfort is my political adviser, as you know, but this time I take my advice from Benito Juárez!"

Juárez's self-effacing patience had won the trust of Álvarez. He spent the night composing a new statement to be issued in Álvarez's name. He pointed out that the Plan of Ayulta did not authorize a military junta in the capital to choose as president of Mexico a man who a few hours before had been persecuting the supporters of the revolution. The Plan was a captive of its enemies! Juárez explained in simple language that the true Plan was intended to liberate the people from the clergy and the military. The patriots who had leaped in to liberate the country, he promised, would finish the revolution Álvarez had begun.

At dawn next day, Juárez was at the printers, helping set into type the revised article. He sent copies to Comonfort, to Ocampo, to Arriaga, to Mata, and all the conspirators who had been with him in New Orleans. He sent copies by swift-riding couriers to the capital as well.

He enclosed a copy in his next letter to Margarita. She would know, now, how he fulfilled his task as representative of the exiles.

To her Juárez mentioned, casually, that the so-called president at Mexico City had appointed him governor of Oaxaca, but he had declined since Carrera had no legal right to offer anybody anything.

"I go now," he added, "to join Álvarez in his march to the capital. We cannot tell what will befall, but I beg, dear wife, that you prepare to make the journey soon to meet me in Mexico City with the children. May this be the last separation we shall ever know! From your husband who loves you . . ."

Álvarez's statement caused consternation in Mexico City. When Juárez returned to Álvarez's head-quarters, he found an agent of Carrera's sitting with Álvarez, commissioned to persuade the old man that Carrera's election was legal.

"Sit down with us," Álvarez said to his secretary. "Explain to Don Campuzano why we cannot accept Santa Anna's confederate as leader of our revolution." He turned to the stranger and added, "Juárez and I see eye to eye in this matter, but he is a scholar and has the language to express my thoughts."

The three men spent an hour together, after which Campuzano departed, fully convinced. He did not even return to the capital to give an account of the result to Carrera.

The next day General Álvarez rode at the head of his troops in the direction of the capital. Benito Juárez, on his old nag, rode as always inconspicuously near the rear. But before they had crossed the state, two other messengers caught up with the troops, bringing messages from Carrera. Again Juárez presented the reasons that Álvarez could not support the men who had seized the capital.

These men were liberals of good faith and they were also convinced that Carrera could not be confirmed as president because his ideas were contrary to the plan of the revolution. Juárez was asked to write a letter to General Carrera urging him to retire to private life. Carrera, on receiving the letter understood that he was being used as a figurehead. He was gone from the capital by the time Comonfort and Ocampo joined Álvarez at Aguala on the border between Guerrero and the state of Mexico.

With Ocampo, when he arrived at Aguala, were his daughter and Mata, newly married. The reunion between Ocampo and Juárez was a happy one. Juárez considered Ocampo the greatest man in Mexico and was overcome with joy to have him at his side.

Juárez had prepared a manifesto for Álvarez to proclaim to the nation and the five men went over it together. On September 24 it was made public.

Álvarez named a council to put into practice the provisions of the Plan of Ayulta. The council was composed of one representative from each state, and Juárez was named to represent Oaxaca. He was also named as one of the three secretaries of the council whose president was the venerable Dr. Gomez Farías. The council would meet on October 4 in the city of

Cuernavaca in the state of Mexico to choose a president.

Great crowds came out to meet the marching troops when finally they crossed into the state of Mexico. Somewhere along the way, Juárez discarded his old boots and white cottons for more formal dress. He entered the pretty little town of Cuernavaca not as private secretary and camp follower of Álvarez's rough and ready army, but as the representative of Oaxaca on the revolutionary council. However, a friend, looking for him along the line to tell him that his wife and children were waiting for him in Cuernavaca found him still in the rear of the troops. The old pack horse assigned to him could not keep up with the high-stepping steeds of Álvarez or of Comonfort, the handsome war hero.

"In any case," he explained, smilingly, "General Álvarez is the acknowledged chief of the revolution and Señor Comonfort is his political adviser."

Juárez knew that Comonfort was not wholly on the side of the revolution, but he never forgot what they owed him. Because of his support Doblado and Degollado, governors of important states, now joined the movement. Besides, Comonfort had been fighting openly for change while the rest of them were still in exile. For this Juárez could accept patiently the self-assurance and arrogance of the man.

Álvarez turned more and more to the "little Indian." Being part Indian, part Negro, the general hesitated to exercise the power he had, and Juárez gave him confidence. They wanted the same kind of world. In their country for hundreds of years only the wealthy, the well-born whites had power, and Comonfort, for all his liberal ideas, belonged to this class.

Yet Juárez felt at home in any society. His shyness about coming forward in Cuernavaca, when the government was being formed, did not spring from lack of confidence. He simply recognized that it was best for their cause to be led by men like Ocampo and Comonfort. However, when he saw that Comonfort hoped to be chosen president, Juárez stood firm. When the secretaries of the council held a meeting to choose a president, he proposed Álvarez and carried the vote. Then he saw to it that Álvarez should ask Ocampo to form the cabinet.

Comonfort was given the post of Secretary of War. The poet, Prieto, lately released from Santa Anna's prison, was made Secretary of the Treasury, Ocampo, Minister of the Interior and Foreign Affairs. That left the posts of Minister of Education and Minister of Justice to be decided. Ocampo insisted that Benito Juárez was the best man in the country for both of these offices. Álvarez agreed. There was nothing for Juárez to do but accept these double duties.

To these four able men, President Álvarez left the task of completing the revolution he had fought for since the days of Morelos. He claimed that he knew nothing about politics and was too old to learn. He would stay in camp with his troops in Cuernavaca and let Comonfort represent him in the capital.

Juárez found a house in the huge, crowded city and moved his family there immediately. The departments of education and justice were enough to keep him busy. Opening new schools, reopening those Santa Anna had closed, meant finding both teachers and money. Organizing tribunals of justice was another matter, he explained to his wife when they talked over his duties together. It was the moment, he said, even before the Congress was elected, to write a new, revolutionary constitution, to set up courts of law that would have power over every class of citizen— whether they were in the army or clergy or simple, ordinary people like themselves.

Margarita did not think her husband an ordinary man. She knew him for what he was, but she smiled and said, "Then why not go and write your law. You are the Minister of Justice, Juárez."

From the first cabinet meeting trouble arose between Ocampo's ideas and those of Comonfort.

As they had often agreed in New Orleans, Ocampo insisted that the clergy must be temporarily deprived of the vote in the Congress. Comonfort objected. He was overruled. The other three men would have excluded the army too, but Comonfort balked. He was Minister of War, he said. Over the army he expected to exercise full power. He would not even discharge the generals who had fought for Santa Anna. Ocampo resigned and went home to his garden.

Prieto and Juárez stayed on—Prieto, because Ocampo wanted him to, Juárez because he would not give up his dream of turning military victory into a political revolution. He would not give up hope of reforming the law. The Indians had waited for three hundred years for justice and a rule of law. Juárez could not disappoint them.

After Comonfort had had his way with the organization of the army, Juárez spoke again about the reform of the law as it affected the army. He spoke as Minister of Justice, not as a private person. Comonfort thought that depriving the clergy and army of their special courts was a mistake "at this time," but Comonfort would not vote against the law. Neither would he vote for it. He simply would not vote at all.

Juárez took the stagecoach to Cuernavaca to consult with President Álvarez, who was on his side. In his portfolio was a precious sheet of paper on which he had written a law abolishing the age-old privilege of the clergy and the army to stand outside the civil law of the land. The sheet contained only a few simple sentences on which Benito Juárez had worked all night long. As he was to say many times afterward, it was not perfect, but it was a challenge to everyone in the government to choose sides. To move toward a better society or to leave Mexico as it was, a country without a final authority of government in which all citizens received equal justice.

"We need your law," Álvarez said, "as we needed Morelos' abolition of slavery a half century ago, when I was young. But before you propose it in the council, Benito, I had better bring my troops to the capital. I smell trouble ahead."

The old man sighed. The fifty years of fighting for freedom were less of a burden to him than this one year of governing. He would not be happy in the palace and neither would his soldiers. "They call my men *pintos*, mountain barbarians. But what must be, must be."

Juárez hurried back to prepare a welcome for the president. A gala performance at the National Theater was announced to honor him. The "nice" people, important people such as the Archbishop and the generals, even some of those who called themselves liberals, decided to spend that evening in their homes. Juárez and Prieto, alone of the leaders of the government, went to the theater with President Álvarez. Comonfort stayed away, as he did five days later when the council met to vote on the law abolishing privileges—the law which from that time to this day is called the *Ley Juárez*.

The poor people, the Indians, living in the crowded slums in back of the Zócalo, loved Álvarez and honored him, and welcomed his battle-scarred soldiers. The wealthy Creoles showed their fear and hatred by threatening revolt and boarding up their windows in fear that the poorly dressed soldiers tramping "their" streets would riot and loot. Actually, four days after the general announced the decree giving the civil courts the right to try any man or woman no matter what his profession or station in life, Álvarez decided to resign. He named Comonfort as temporary head of the government.

Álvarez made only two conditions: the old law abolishing slavery forever must be reaffirmed, and the *Ley Juárez*, received with such enthusiasm by the common people and the progressives over the nation, must never be repealed. By this last act before he marched his troops back to Guerrero, Álvarez saved the basic goal of the revolution. The "men of Ayulta" were out of the government, but the moderates who came into power under Comonfort were forced against their will to support Juárez's law. Public opinion was too strong in its favor to allow the law to be nullified. Doblado, the general who had threatened revolt ten days earlier, now gave the *Ley Juárez* his strong support. Benito Juárez was to remember this with gratitude in the years to come.

Comonfort formed a new cabinet for his term as temporary president. Elections would be held as soon as the Congress had finished writing a new constitution. He did not offer Juárez a place in the cabinet, but offered instead to appoint him governor of Oaxaca once more. Juárez accepted because he knew that opposition was being stirred up there against the *Ley Juarez*. The army and the clergy were demanding their old privileges, refusing to answer the summons of the civil courts. There had even been reports of fighting in the streets.

Early in January 1856, Juárez and his family made the journey south to Oaxaca, Margarita and the girls in a black carriage, Juárez and his sons, Bene and Pepe, on horseback.

The governor was met at Etla by a large body of his supporters and escorted through the streets of Oaxaca to the cathedral. But this time there was no Bishop to give the oath of office and celebrate the inauguration with a *Te Deum*. The doors of the cathedral were closed to Benito Juárez, author of the law.

Juárez quietly took the oath of office without benefit of clergy. The break between the Church and the civil government was made final. Juárez spent the rest of the year restoring the schools and the neglected roads, and reforming the militia into a national guard of the citizens. He waited anxiously for the work of Congress on the constitution to be ended, when the *Ley Juárez*, which up to now had been only a decree, would come into full force.

"There were citizens in the state," he wrote in his memoirs, "who did not intend that there should be a democratic victory."

And when they started a rebellion, Juárez's national guard put it down with arms. A young man from the Institute was wounded in the fighting. His name, Porforio Díaz, is an important one in Juarez' life and in the history of Mexico. In 1856, however, Díaz was known simply as a young Mixtec Indian, a brave student for whom the governor sought the best doctor he could find.

At last in the spring of 1857, the constitution was finished. It was not perfect but one did the best one could. Elections were called and Comonfort, candidate for president, persuaded Benito Juárez to run for the presidency of the Supreme Court, an office which, under the new constitution, carried with it the responsibility of serving as vice-president of the nation.

"You will help me calm down certain pretensions that are dangerous in the difficult crises through which we are passing," Comonfort wrote, "and finally because you are informed on the situation, your knowledge of it would help you to carry on the business if, as president of the Supreme Court, you should have to take upon yourself the command of the nation—because of the failure of my health or some other grave cause necessitated this step."

Crisis. Danger of Comonfort's resignation. The letter had an ominous ring. Juárez accepted the call to serve in the capital because, he said, "My convictions put me in a position to cooperate in every way in the development of the glorious revolution of Ayulta."

On October 27, 1857, Benito Juárez, fifty-one years of age, left Oaxaca for Mexico City. He left his family in a comfortable house in Oaxaca. To be separated once more from his wife and children was a hardship. He would look for a suitable house for them in the city and return for them as soon as possible.

He appointed his friend Díaz Ordaz acting governor and quietly took the stagecoach across the wild mountainous country. Juárez never saw Oaxaca again.

∞ 12 ∞

In Defense of the Future

On December 1, 1857, Comonfort and Juárez were sworn in to the offices for which they had been elected. The ceremony was of necessity conducted without the traditional *Te Deum* in the cathedral because the Church authorities had issued a decree excommunicating all who swore loyalty to the *Ley Juárez* and the new Constitution.

The government had been under fire even before the inauguration of Comonfort. Miguel Miramón, acting for the priesthood and the generals, had raised the cry of "Religion and Privileges" and threatened the return of Santa Anna unless Comonfort and his moderate followers abandoned Juárez's law. The troops in the fortress at Puebla, less than 100 miles east of Mexico City, gave Miramón open support. Another army of 2,000, under the reactionary General Zuloaga, hovered around the capital itself ready to overthrow the government. Rumblings had come too, from the other side. Governor Juan Baz and Ramírez, poet, writer, teacher, and friend of Juárez, seeing the weakness of the constitutional government, had announced themselves in favor of a temporary revolutionary dictatorship to force real religious liberty and distribution of land to the farmers.

To Juárez reforms by force seemed almost as dangerous as no reforms at all. He was not an enemy of religion but was only against the interference of the Church in the civil government. He was aware of the difficult position of President Comonfort, pressed as he was by his extremely devout mother, by the reactionary generals he had insisted on retaining in the army, and by his wealthy friends. However, Juárez wrote to his wife in Oaxaca, "Comonfort is strong in his devotion to the Constitution. He hesitates to act because the government is still weak."

As Minister of Justice, Juárez found the government without money to pay for judges to enforce the law. As Minister of the Interior, he was responsible for internal order—but had no funds to pay enough soldiers to keep the peace. He was kept busy trying to put down minor rebellions breaking out here and there over the nation.

The conspiracy against the Constitution itself, the threat of the Church and the army to rise against the new government was talked about all over the city; still Juárez did not question Comonfort's loyalty. True, the president had not really been part of the

New Orleans revolution. He had opposed the *Ley Juárez*. However, he had not voted against it and when he was elected president he had chosen strong liberals to help him govern.

Two weeks later, on December 15, Governor Baz of the Federated District of Mexico repented of his part in the growing conspiracy. He appeared before the Congress and revealed the plan to overthrow the government by force. Baz named Manuel Payno, Secretary of the Treasury, and General Zuloaga as the leaders of the conspiracy. He had been present at a meeting between Zuloaga and Comonfort where, even before his inauguration, Comonfort had pledged support to Zuloaga. But of this he made no mention. He contented himself with saying to the Congress, "This is the last time you will meet as legislators."

Juárez, questioned by the Congress, drew on his usual optimism and attempted to calm the legislators. Action against Payno and Zuloaga was postponed until a grand jury could sift the facts.

Payno was indicted by the grand jury and the next day Juárez heard the truth from Comonfort's own lips.

"We must change our political position, Benito," the president said. "I want you to take part and go along with me."

Juárez's answer is recorded in his diary: "Choose whatever side you like, for I have already chosen mine. Truly I wish you happiness on the road you are going to take, but I shall not go with you."

During that night Zuloaga's brigade entered Mexico City and posted broadsides declaring the Constitution and the *Ley Juárez* abolished.

When Juárez arrived at the palace next morning, he was met by an armed guard acting under the orders of Comonfort and put under arrest. The other liberal members of the cabinet—Prieto, Manuel Ruíz, and de la Fuente—promptly resigned. They, too, had been kept in the dark about Comonfort's decision to exchange his title of constitutional president for that of a dictator.

The first victim of the conspiracy was Benito Juárez, who had chosen the side he was on. The first important military engagement was in Juárez's own state, Oaxaca. Reactionary troops came down from the mountains shouting "Religion and Privileges. Down with Juárez's Law." They took part of the city. But Governor Ordaz, Porfirio Díaz and other officers from the Institute drove the insurgents out in bloody, house-to-house fighting. While Juárez was still imprisoned in the palace, the war in defense of the Constitution had begun.

Zuloaga and Payno had meanwhile been joined by the reactionary Miramón. They were impatient with Comonfort's hesitation. They demanded that he abolish the *Ley Juárez* by decree. When he refused, a few priests and generals met in secret and swore in General Zuloaga as their president.

Comonfort saw that he had been tricked. He released Juárez from prison.

Under the darkness of night, January 11, 1858, Manuel Ruíz and Benito Juárez slipped away on foot. Juárez's only luggage was a copy of the Constitution which Zuloaga that day had declared abolished. The new government had lasted only a month and a half!

"We won't be separated much longer," he had assured Margarita in a hurried letter to Oaxaca. "I will send for you and the children as soon as we have established a seat of government. I am your husband who loves you."

No one, least of all Benito Juárez, could have guessed that "establishing a seat of government" was going to cost four long years of struggle and sacrifice. The need to escape capture and total defeat was, within a few weeks, to drive Juárez out of the country. Later he would re-enter and establish a temporary seat of the legitimate government in the large port city of Veracruz. Before the slow return to the capital could take place, thousands of lives would be lost, cities sacked, and families divided.

After leaving the capital on January 11, Juárez and Ruíz slept for four nights in the fields. They ate when they could find a household friendly to their cause. After covering thirty miles this way on foot, they ventured to take a mail coach to the village of Querétaro. From there another coach was about to leave for Guanajuato, a little mining town in the mountains to the west. Ruíz had mentioned earlier that this was where the liberals in the government were planning to gather. As the coach rattled away from Querétaro, church bells and firing of skyrockets announced that the town had gone over to Zuloaga.

Degollado, a justice of the Supreme Court, was waiting in Guanajuato when Juárez arrrived. Prieto (disguised as a muleteer), Ocampo, and others joined them a few days later. The new arrivals reported that Comonfort, rejected by the Church and army, had rallied a few troops to defend the elected government, but had been unable to hold them. The resistance against Zuloaga had collapsed. Zuloaga had taken possession of the palace amid a wild ringing of church bells. And Comonfort? He had left the city with his family, a ruined man headed for exile.

From Veracruz, on February 1, Comonfort officially resigned, naming the elected vice-president, Benito Juárez, president of the Republic of Mexico.

On the seventh of February, when Comonfort sailed for New York, Juárez had already chosen his cabinet. He was the legal head of a government without a capital, without funds, without an organized army. But he was the guardian of the Constitution, of liberty and the future.

He wrote in his diary: "Under extremely difficult conditions the son of Guelatao attained the supreme magistry."

❧ **13** ❧

"A Little Indian by the Name of Juárez"

Mexico, in 1857, was just coming into a sense of true nationhood. By European or United States' standards it was a hopelessly backward country; but its newspapers boasted "gossip columns" as ruthless as any in our papers today. It was a gossip columnist who mentioned the flight of Benito Juárez to Guanajuato: "A little Indian by the name of Juárez, who calls himself president of Mexico, has arrived in this city."

A little Indian? Yes. Four fifths of the inhabitants of the country were of Indian ancestry, yet Benito Juárez was the first to rise to high office in their native land. *Calls* himself president? He *was* president by every legal right. It was to defend this legality, this rule of law that he had left his family and his home and risked his life. "Government by consent of the governed" had given Juárez the title of president. His authority to rule was accepted by the great majority of the people and by the governors of ten important states and Juárez intended to fulfill this mandate.

The League of Governors, formed to defend Juárez and the Constitution, included such men as Doblado of Guadalajara; the tall, quiet scholar Degollado of Michoacán; Zamora of Veracruz, General Parrodi of Jalisco, and General Juan Álvarez, again governor of Guerrero. These men and other leaders accepted Juárez as the legal president until such time as peaceful elections could be held again. In his cabinet were men of national fame—Ocampo, Prieto, Romero, Manuel Ruíz. Only Mexico City and the regular army were in the hands of the enemy. The territory surrounding the capital was in control of the old and respected League of Governors.

From Guanajuato, on January 19, President Juárez issued a manifesto to the nation, defending the Constitution and condemning those who attempted to destroy it. He said in part: "They have invoked the sacred name of our religion—and have sought to destroy at one blow the liberty that Mexicans have won at the cost of sacrifices of every kind." He promised that Mexico would be governed neither by one man alone nor by any faction but by this Constitution. He asked for cooperation of the Mexican people and the protection of divine providence.

Juárez named General Parrodi commander of the military forces. Parrodi proposed to draw the regular troops out of the city and away from their base with one detachment of his 7,000 volunteers. Meanwhile,

Doblado, with the other half, would attack the capital. Juárez was so sure of success that he issued a proclamation, promising to reconvene Congress and hold elections for a new president as soon as Mexico City was retaken. His one desire, he said, was to resign power. "I have no wish to retain it one day longer than the brief time required to establish peace under the Constitution."

While waiting the result of Parrodi's campaign, Juárez was persuaded, as a safety measure, to move the government to the larger city of Guadalajara.

They left Guanajuato in the dead of night in large black carriages with the curtains drawn and guards carrying torches to light their road. To Prieto, Secretary of the Treasury, it appeared that the silent people on the wayside were watching a funeral procession—the funeral of liberty.

To Guadalajara then, on the twelfth day of March, a messenger came from Parrodi. The army had been badly defeated. Five hundred soldiers had been killed. With only 3,000 troops left to him, the general was on his way to Guadalajara. A day later news came that Doblado, beaten in a skirmish before he reached Mexico City, had withdrawn his half of the total number of troops from the war.

The whole plan of attack was shattered. Consternation spread among the people of Guadalajara. The members of the cabinet were despondent, but Juárez took the news with his usual calm.

"After all," he said, "the misfortune in a battle is bad, but it is one of the all-too-common hazards of war. We will conquer in the end, because democracy is the destiny of Mexico." He asked Prieto, the poet, to prepare a statement of confidence in the country's future.

Even while they were talking over the wording of the manifesto, Colonel Landa's supposedly loyal regiment rebelled inside Guadalajara, the city Landa had been sent to guard. Soldiers marched in the streets shouting Zuloaga's slogans, "Long live the Army! Long live Religion! Long live the Privileges!"

No sooner had Prieto retired to a back room in a little house across the plaza, than Landa's troops broke into the palace and captured Juárez and Ocampo and all the ministers. They herded the unarmed men into one big room and held them there, prisoners.

The hostile troops and the priests who cheered them on surrounded the palace grounds. To swell their numbers, they opened the nearby prison.

Prieto, locked in a dark little room with his writing materials, heard the uproar and rushed into the street. He heard a robed priest urging the soldiers to kill Juárez, "author of the infamous law against religion." Prieto went up to him and demanded to share the fate of the president. A blow on the head with a rifle butt was the reply. His unconscious form was thrust into the hall with the other captives. When he regained consciousness, Ocampo, his close friend, was bending over him, tying a bandage around his head.

"It's said we're going to be shot within the hour," Melchor Ocampo whispered.

The hour was almost past when they heard the tramping of feet and shouting in the corridor.

"They are coming to kill us!" someone cried.

There was a scuffle outside the door. A few loyal soldiers had made their way into the palace. The prisoners could hear them being driven back. The head of the mutineers pounded on the door and a loud voice demanded that Juárez order the surrender of his forces. Juárez refused. "As a prisoner I cannot give any commands."

The quiet answer evidently puzzled Colonel Landa. He retired for consultation and the prisoners were left all night in darkness, without food or water, with armed guards outside the door.

At dawn the tramp of feet began again.

"Shoulder arms!" The order could only mean one thing. The firing squad . . .

Benito Juárez advanced calmly toward the door, undoing the buttons of his formal, double-breasted frock coat as he walked.

"Ready!"

"Aim!"

Juárez had one hand on the door latch. He flung open the door, raised his head, and stood quietly waiting for death.

But the order to fire was never given. At this moment Prieto threw himself in front of the president.

"Put up your guns!" he shouted. "Brave men are not murderers!"

The poet talked and talked, while the firing squad and the prisoner stood equally transfixed by the eloquent torrent of words. Liberty, justice, loyalty to the Constitution, to Juárez, the son of the people, their honor as Mexicans—Prieto made every possible appeal.

Benito Juárez had not moved. He was still a perfect target for the loaded guns. But the attitude of the soldiers changed. The sergeant lowered his rifle. Uncertainly, the rest did the same. One man burst into tears.

The soldiers swore they would not shed the blood of the president and vanished down the corridor.

Juárez forgot his reserve and threw his arms around Prieto and called him the savior of the revolution. The poet sobbed with relief.

The mayor of the city was helpless against the military, but he pointed out to Colonel Landa who had led the mutiny that Parrodi's army was marching toward Guadalajara. Reluctantly Landa consented to move his troops three miles outside the city if Juárez would move his trouble-making government from Guadalajara that night.

Juárez did not say yes. He did not say no. He turned his attention to the manifesto Prieto had drawn up. He was determined to deliver it to the nation before he prepared to leave the city.

"Whether or not we lose battles, the sacred cause we defend is invincible. . . . Democracy is the destiny of humanity in the future, freedom is the indestructible weapon. . . . With these beliefs, which are the life of my heart, with this faith, the only title that raises my humble person to the greatness of my task, the incidents of war are contemptible; the idea is above the domain of cannon."

At three thirty in the morning, Benito Juárez moved his government out of Guadalajara southwest toward Colima and the shores of the Pacific. Carrying the Constitution, Juárez rode with Ocampo and Ruíz in a carriage; the rest of the cabinet members followed on horseback. The procession had as escort a small troop of infantry and a body of thirty cavalrymen under the ardent young revolutionary, Lieutenant Leandro Valle. It was a strange journey through the danger-infested night. Valle and Achilles Collin, a young Frenchman Valle had met in his student days in Paris, rode beside the carriage and, whenever the pace of travel allowed, talked about the ideas of the French Revolutionary writers and poets with Ocampo and Juárez. The courage of the fleeing fugitives was remarkable.

The conversation continued at a wayside inn where they stopped for breakfast. When Juárez received a message that Landa, with a much larger force than their own, was hot on their trail, Lieutenant Valle rushed out to deploy his troops. Firing broke out in the street. Juárez and the others moved to the flat roof of the inn. On the rooftop a small incident took place that Benito Juárez was never to forget. Collin noticed an enemy sharpshooter hiding behind a bush in the garden. He borrowed a rifle from a soldier, took aim, and shot the man dead. Then he returned the rifle and quietly rejoined his friends.

"Well done," Ocampo said.

Collin replied, "Señor, a man is always a man. How is it that you, one of the great advocates of justice and democracy can congratulate me on having killed a man?"

Juárez sighed. The young man had touched a sore spot. How could the better society they longed for come by killing?

But Ocampo had an answer. "It is not because you have killed a man. On the contrary, it is because you have saved many by making this one a vicitim in urgent necessity, without hatred, without pride."

The soldiers drove the attackers back, but Juárez knew they would return tomorrow with more reinforcements. Once more the "Government of Mexico" could find safety only in flight. There was no time for conversation that night as they covered the miles to the city of Colima, near the coast.

Colima was small, unfortified, indefensible. There was, besides, no army left to fight for it . . . News came that Parrodi had been defeated in a battle at Guadalajara and had been forced to surrender. When an invitation came from General Zamora, governor of the state of Veracruz, to make his capital the seat of the national government, Juárez called the cabinet together. He presented the question and then silently listened to the arguments of his ministers. There was much to be said for going to Veracruz. The populace was staunch, the governor brave. It was the largest port in the country, well fortified. But there was the distance to be traveled. They had seen what it was to travel through hostile territory. And how could armies be raised if they were off in one corner of Mexico?

Juárez turned to Señor Santos Degollado, who had come to Colima to offer his services as commander in chief and minister of war.

"The military is only an arm of the government," the scholar answered. "There is no government to protect unless the legally elected president and Constitution survive. I will stay in Colima with General Iniestra to raise an army."

"Veracruz, then, will be the seat of government." Juárez made the decision in his usual quiet manner. "But crossing Mexico just now is an unnecessary risk. There is another way—long and roundabout . . ." He paused, remembering the journey from New Orleans to Álvarez's camp just three years ago. Then, they had no constitution, only a plan; no government except in their dreams. But he had been there, he knew every step of the way. "We will go by sea, Señores. A steamer to Panama, across the Isthmus by rail, Havana, New Orleans, Veracruz."

Like a family on holiday, they made their way to the port town, waited a week until a large and crowded American steamer hove to. On April 25, they were in New Orleans, where Juárez and Ocampo tried to show the others the boardinghouse where the plan of liberty and democracy had been drafted. But the house had been torn down.

On May 4, 1858, a twenty-one-gun salute from the Castle of San Juan de Ulloa welcomed the president of the Republic of Mexico.

All Veracruz turned out to meet the ship with flowers and banners and drums. With cries of "*Viva Juárez! Viva Mexico!*" The legitimate government of Mexico had a home again on Mexican soil.

In the house Zamora had provided for the government, Juárez sat down that night to read dispatches from Degollado and another from the troubled state of Oaxaca where his own supporters were fighting a little civil war of their own. The dispatches could wait until tomorrow to be answered. He dipped his pen in the inkwell to write to Margarita. From her he had received no letter, though a postscript on one of the Oaxacan messages told him she and the children were well.

14

"*Beyond the Domain of a Cannon*"

In Oaxaca, on Calle Independencia, an Indian boy tied the bridle of his burro to the iron fence outside the Maza house. He pulled the bell rope with confidence. Doña Margarita Juárez was expecting him.

Since Juárez left for Mexico City, Margarita had been living in the house that had belonged to her parents. At first her brother had been there to take some of the burden from her shoulders, but a few months ago José María had died quite suddenly of pneumonia. Now she and the eight children were here alone. The baby crawling happily on the floor had her first birthday the week that José María died.

At the sound of the bell, Margarita crossed the patio and went in to the yard to admit the visitor. "I measure time by my children's birthdays," she said to herself. "What else is there for me, living this way, alone?"

"You sent for me, Señora?" the young man asked

in very careful, schoolboy Spanish.

"Are you Félipe from Guelatao?" Margarita was surprised to see so young a burro driver. Josefa, who had recommended him, had said he was experienced and responsible.

"*Sí*, Señora, from Guelatao. Josefa Juárez told my father you wished to make a journey. We have six burros at your disposal. There were not eight to be had on the mountain. My father and I will be your burro men."

"Come in." With the baby in her arms, Margarita led the way to the patio, pushed her sewing off a bench and spread out a map of Mexico. "Here is Oaxaca," she said, "and here is Veracruz. That's where we must go."

"Sí, Señora, to *El Presidente*." The young man leaned closer to study the map. "We go by way of Puebla?"

Margarita shook her head. She had given careful thought to the plan. There was no open road that would be safe for the Juárez family to travel. Every highway beyond Oaxaca was in the hands of the enemy. Even in Oaxaca it would not be wise to let anyone know of her journey. She pointed again to the map.

"We shall have to go straight as a bird flies, across the mountains. Six burros is all you could find? Very well. Beno or Pepe and I can walk. Manuela can hold the baby. We can pack the food in hanging baskets, two to each burro. Food and a few clothes."

"But, Señora, there are no roads over the mountains. Scarcely a cattle trail! And there are snakes in the underbrush and wildcats."

"Don't you have machetes? And revolvers?"

"Of course. A rough journey like this is all in the day's work for my father and me. But for the wife of El Presidente!"

"Do you think Señor Juárez is having an easy time? I am his wife and it is right for me to be with him."

"Sí, Señora." The Indian made no more objections.

They set a date for departure and Margarita gave him the money she had scraped together for the burros and the carrying baskets.

"Till Wednesday," she said almost gaily and watched the boy until he was out of sight.

The distance to Veracruz on the map was 150 miles; but Juárez's friend at the Institute had warned that the journey on the mountain trail would be almost double that. As Margarita marketed for food and sorted clothes during the next three days, she must have had moments of great anxiety. Not about her guides—they were Zapotec, her husband's people. But what if they lost the trail? What if one of the children got sick? What if the fires they would build at night failed to keep the wild animals at bay?

"Don't worry," her husband always said when things looked black. She would not worry once the family was under the same roof again. Ever since she heard that Juárez was safe in Veracruz, she had determined to make this journey. *Three hundred miles, ten miles a day,* through the wilderness. In a month the separation would be at an end.

On the first day of July, Margarita Juárez and her eight children, with only the escort of two Zapotec burro drivers, walked into the picturesque seaport of Veracruz. They had stopped outside the city on a beach and washed and changed to the clean clothes so carefully hoarded on the mountain journey. Margarita did not want her husband to be ashamed of their appearance. However, no amount of care could hide the deep fatigue of the trip.

The little procession walked past carriages with elegantly dressed ladies, past sailors from the foreign ships in port, past dark-skinned longshoremen pushing heavy carts, past the market and the churches to the large house on the plaza, flying the flag of Mexico.

The guards at the gate looked at Margarita with puzzled expressions. Even in friendly Veracruz there had been more than one attempt on the life of the president. And all sorts of masquerades were adopted by spies to get into the government offices. Because of Juárez's well-known sympathy with the poor, a favorite trick was to come with some appealing tale of hardship. One had to be careful. However, in spite of her flapping sandals, with the soles worn through and the jagged tear in her reboza, the blond woman with all those children did not have the look of a spy or a beggar.

The guard spoke to her politely. "Señor Juárez is occupied with his ministers, Señora. Another time, perhaps, he will give you an audience."

Margarita was almost dropping with weariness, but she managed a smile. "Tell the president, if you please, that his wife and children have arrived."

For Juárez, the two months he had spent in Veracruz had been very difficult. There were few soldiers on the streets and little fighting. Governor Zamora kept order and the people, largely of Indian and Negro ancestry, were loyal and sympathetic to the government. Juárez and his ministers were safe, for the moment at least, but in the harbor Spanish and French warships hovered threateningly. They were there to collect the revenues from the custom duties for old debts and for new loans negotiated in Mexico City where every European government still kept its embassy open. Zuloaga and his popular new general, Miramón, could get all the money they needed from these foreigners and from the Church authorities. The legitimate government in Veracruz had no funds to pay the thousands of soldiers who had volunteered to fight under Degollado or under Álvarez or Porfirio Díaz in Oaxaca.

The United States government was wavering. The pro-slavery President, James Buchanan, was dickering both with the rebels at Mexico City and with the government at Veracruz. With a greed "bordering on mania" Buchanan was trying to get even more of Mexico's land to add to that lost by Santa Anna. For Lower California and the state of Sonora, he offered money and guns. Benito Juárez's government was determined not to give "a palm's breadth" of territory, but Juárez had sent Mata, Ocampo's son-in-law to Washington. There must be some other way than giving up land to get a loan from the Republic to the north. If not a loan, at least recognition of the legally elected government.

Meanwhile, one battle after another had been lost in the rich central section of the country. After the loss of Guadalajara, San Luis Potosí, Morelia, and Puebla had fallen into the hands of the enemy. The people in the countryside remained loyal to Juárez, but even there, many churches were turned into fortresses for Zuloaga's benefit.

To add to Juárez's personal anxieties, fighting had broken out again in the streets of Oaxaca. It was not until Margarita and the children arrived at the gates of the government house that he knew them to be alive and well. In the home Zamora found for them to live in, Benito Juárez found the strength to endure.

Six months later, in January 1859, Miguel Miramón, twenty-six years old, handsome, brave, and dashing, took the presidency from Zuloaga. A month later he managed to lead an army across the low marshlands outside Veracruz and to lay siege to the city.

It was a dangerous moment for the government forces. British warships were added to the French in the harbor, but Degollado made the most of Miramón's absence. Swiftly he advanced on several cities and then marched on Mexico City itself.

Degollado did not have enough forces or artillery to capture the capital city, but his threat had the effect of lifting the siege of Veracruz. Miramón beat a retreat, out of the fever-infested marshes on to the road to the capital.

Just as Miramón lifted the siege and the country people up and down the shore were rushing food to the hungry inhabitants of Veracruz, a United States' battleship steamed around the castle of San Juan de Ulloa. Aboard was Robert Milligan McLane, American diplomat empowered to recognize Juárez's government if he saw fit, and to negotiate a loan at the price of giving up Lower California and rights of transit for a railroad across the narrow neck of land in the south. Juárez insisted that he could not consider negotiations unless he was recognized as the legal head of state. A treaty was only possible, he said, between sovereign states. McLane gave in, and the long and bitter negotiations began which were to come to nothing in the end.

The military news was bad again. Degollado had been defeated near the capital at Tacubaya by the ruthless bandit Márquez. Against all rules of war, Miramón ordered Márquez to shoot the officers he held as prisoner. Márquez went beyond the order and murdered soldiers, medical students, women, and children in the area. For this he earned the name of the "Tiger of Tacubaya."

It was in the shadow of this military defeat that a treaty with the United States' envoy was finally consented to. Even then Ocampo and Juárez would not include the sale of a foot of Mexican land. The compromise settled upon in the treaty was a free right of way "forever" across the Isthmus of Tehuantepec with a free port at each end. On this land the United States government would have the right to build a railroad and to enforce its own laws. For this granted right, the United States would negotiate a loan to Mexico to buy arms. Juárez hated this treaty. President Buchanan of the United States at this time was a pro-slavery man and Juárez feared that slaveholders would come in, but Juárez was silent when his entire cabinet voted for the treaty.

The treaty itself would not come into force until it was ratified by the United States Senate. When it was brought up in the Senate there were long and furious arguments. The more Juárez heard from his agents in Washington, the less he liked the news. He was not sorry when, after almost a year of debate, the treaty failed to get the approval of the United States government. When it was proposed to give the United States more time, Juárez quietly but firmly said no.

However, as the civil war dragged on, with neither side able to win, "For what are we fighting?" the poor people began to ask themselves. To defend a constitution whose promises had yet to be fulfilled? True, they had the law Benito Juárez had written and they had Juárez, but reforms could not be delayed.

In July 1859, a year and a half after Comonfort and Juárez had been sworn in, the president, with the consent of his cabinet, issued the first of a number of decrees. The first was absolute separation of Church and State without which religion itself could not be free. Then the vast, unused church lands and buildings not used as houses of worship were nationalized. The common grazing land in the villages was returned to the Indians. These reform decrees raised the spirits of the people. They were the turning point of the war.

However, as the constitutional government developed strength, the danger of European intervention became ever more threatening. The following year, in the spring of 1860, the British presented a scheme for ending the war by compromise. Miramón and Juárez would both resign. The Constitution would be abandoned for a new one. The foreign powers to whom such a large debt was owed would be glad to name a new president. Matthew of Great Britain persuaded Santos Degollado to join in the scheme. Worn out by defeats and harassed by lack of funds to pay his soldiers, the gentle scholar wrote to Juárez begging him to resign "for the sake of peace."

"If the question were whether I were to remain in power or not," Juárez answered, "the decent and dignified course would be for me to retire from the post I occupy; but it is not so. If I were to abandon my post . . . I would descend voluntarily to the level of the rebels and be as criminal as Don Miguel Miramón . . ."

Juárez dismissed Degollado and gave the command of the armies to González Ortega; but he never forgot the service which the gentle and troubled Degollado had given the Republic. Ortega was a better commander than Degollado, however, and the tide of victory was coming in.

Miramón was not ready to admit defeat. He besieged Veracruz for a second time, and arranged for guns and ammunition to be brought in by sea. Two ships, purchased from Spain, were fitted out in Havana. They approached the Mexican coast fully armed, without flying any flag. Juarez proclaimed them pirate ships. The government's fleet which consisted of two small fishing boats gave chase.

Under international law, a pirate ship can be halted and seized as a prize by the ships of any nation. A United States frigate in the harbor took up the chase. When the ships refused an order to stop, the United States captain overtook the vessels, forced them to halt, and sent boarding parties aboard. The two boats were taken to New Orleans as prizes of the sea—pirate ships.

The Maritime Court afterward returned the ships to Spain, but the action saved Veracruz. Without ammunition, Miramón was compelled to lift his siege.

Miramón's retreat in this year of 1860 was through liberated areas, hostile to his cause. Every city except the capital was free. Doblado was back in the field, hurrying to join Ortega outside Mexico City; Díaz and Álvarez were on the march from the south; Zaragoza from the east. The forces loyal to Juárez were closing in on all sides. There was unity in the air and a will to win.

Degollado, the former general, governor of an important state who had been dismissed from his command, was unable to keep out of the fight while his country was in danger. He had quietly re-enlisted as a private in the ranks. And now, as a private, was held prisoner by Miramón.

Miramón knew his dwindling forces no longer had a chance to hold Mexico City. He took his share of the fortune stolen from British envoys and hidden in the city. With that as a nest egg for further adventures, Manuel Miramón embarked safely on a French merchant ship about to sail for Paris. His departure went almost unnoticed—it was to mean misfortune for the future of Mexico.

Zuloaga and Márquez the Tiger also scented trouble. They decided to flee while there was still time and escaped to the mountains with their bands of bandits.

On January 1, 1861, Ortega's army of 10,000 marched into the capital. The military victory was complete.

The populace turned out to cheer the dashing figure of the general. As he rode toward the Zócalo in the rain of flowers and clatter of brass bands, Ortega caught sight of the now-free Degollado among the spectators. He halted the parade, embraced the deposed warrior, and handed him the flag to carry—the precious red, green, and white of liberty! Together, the two generals rode at the head to the procession to take over the national palace in the name of President Benito Juárez and the legitimate Republic.

Word of the sudden victory was brought to Veracruz by a hard-riding courier. The state house was deserted. Juárez and his wife and most of the cabinet ministers were at the Opera House attending a performance of Bellini's opera *I Puritani.*

The courier, exhausted, stumbled into the opera box with his message. Juárez rose; the players stood still in their places on the stage; the orchestra was silent. In a low, quiet voice, Juárez read the bulletin announcing the end of the war. It was one of the great moments of Juárez's life. He stood in utter silence, like a bronze statue while the voices filled the Opera House with one great shout—"Viva Juárez! Viva Mexico!"

The orchestra played the "Marseilles," the song of the revolution to all people, as suitable to Mexico as to the French of the Revolutionary period.

March on. March on to victory! Juárez and his family, Ocampo, Prieto, Ramirez, and the others rode back to the capital in hired carriages. The journey took a week. Ortega had time to prepare a second and larger triumphant procession when the president re-entered the capital to cries of "Viva Juárez! Viva la Constitución!"

But the triumph of justice and the law was destined to be a victory that did not bring peace.

‎⚬15‎⚬

"Cinco de Mayo"

President Juárez issued a proclamation pardoning all except the leaders of the rebellion; but the disorder, the killing, was by no means over. One of Juárez's first acts on January 11, 1861, was to call for an election for the office of president. All through the war years the fact that he was the legal head of the government only because of Comonfort's conspiracy had stayed in his mind. Now the people must have a chance to choose either him or someone else.

Two other candidates ran against Juárez; Ortega, the military leader, and de Tejada, who had helped write the decrees of the Reform. Benito Juárez did not campaign at all through the months required to choose electors and a congress to count the votes; he merely said that if the people wanted him he would serve. Six months later on June 11, 1861, Benito Juárez was declared the elected president of a free Mexico.

All during this six-month period he was discouragedly faced with the appalling devastation of his country. The needs of the people and the burden of foreign debt on the one hand, and the empty treasury on the other occupied all his waking thoughts. To pay the interest on the debts contracted by both sides in three years of civil war took all the revenues.

The money from the sale of Church lands was so meager that the government did not even have funds to pay the 3,000 soldiers in the national army. So Zuloaga and the hated Márquez with their followers roamed over the countryside, robbing and burning and killing since there was no one to stop them.

New schools had to be opened, old ones repaired. A railroad between Mexico City and Veracruz was needed to open new trade.

Juárez applied again to the United States for a loan. It was refused. But, he said to himself, there might be hope at a future date. Abraham Lincoln had been elected and he was a good man. Juárez sent Romero from Washington to call on the President-elect at Springfield, Illinois, and received Lincoln's promise to "do everything in his power to deal justly with Mexico. He considered that country a friendly and sister nation."

Juárez's heart warmed to the obscure, homely lawyer, like himself a son of the people. But it was clear to him after receiving Romero's report and also a letter from Lincoln after the secession of the southern states that Abraham Lincoln was in trouble. He would soon be fighting a war for survival in his own turbulent land. Putting aside all hope of financial help from the United States, Juárez begged his own Congress for money. He urged General Ortega to move against the outlaws with what forces he had. Ortega replied that he could not without supplies and equipment.

On May 30, 1861, one of Márquez's gunmen, with a small troop on horseback, forced his way into the *hacienda* of Melchor Ocampo, who had gone home for a long rest. Except for his Indian housekeeper, Ocampo was alone in the big house. The outlaws seized him and carried him off across the country to Márquez's camp.

The captive was led from one village to another. He passed several friends on the way, but they were helpless. There were no police, no federal soldiers in the neighborhood. On the fourth day after the kidnapping, Ocampo was taken into a field and shot. By Márquez's orders the dead body was hung from a tree limb for all to see.

The assassination of the gentle patriot, the closest friend of the president, caused an uproar in the capital. Crowds of outraged citizens came out in the streets demanding vengeance for Ocampo's murder, the immediate execution of all rebels in the prison awaiting trial.

"I will do everything possible to have the assassins punished according to law," Juárez said from the palace balcony, "but I will never tolerate violence against accused persons who are under the protection of the law."

The sacred trust of law of a civilized society, remained uppermost in Juárez's mind. He would have gone down to the streets to quiet the mob, but General Valle was at the prison door ahead of him. Leandro Valle had defended Juárez from capture in the early days of the war. He had gone through three years of brutal fighting and now risked his life once more by facing the citizens storming the prison.

While Valle was defending the lives of rebel enemies, Degollado was pleading for permission to go in pursuit of Márquez. The Congress, moved by his eloquent plea, voted extraordinary powers to Juárez to raise funds for the expedition by forced loans. This was done.

Degollado set out with a small force for the mountain trail where the murderers had last been seen. He left Mexico City on June 11, the same day that Juárez was declared the elected president. Two days later Ocampo's mutilated body was brought to the capital for burial.

Leandro Valle, with a well-equiped force, went to join Degollado. A week later both men were dead. Degollado, "the soldier of the people, the fighter who never lost hope in the cause of justice and liberty," had fallen into the hands of a guerrilla band who killed him on the spot.

Prieto delivered his funeral oration.

"You who trembled at the tears of a child, you who imposed on yourself every privation lest you squander the pesos of the poor, you were the Saint of the Revolution...."

Valle had 800 men. They were surprised on a mountain pass by the combined forces of Márquez and Zuloaga. Guerrillas shot Valle as "a traitor to religion." Most of his men died trying to defend him. Among them was Achilles Collin, the young Frenchman who had come from his homeland to defend freedom in a distant land.

Panic now struck the leaders who had shouted "Viva Juárez! Viva Mexico!" with such enthusiasm six months before. Juárez was forced to carry on the legal government by decree.

What was most needed was money to raise an army sufficient to rid the country of the 2,000 outlaws. But every peso raised by taxes or customs duties was seized by European governments in payment of interest on war debts, debts incurred chiefly by Miramón's European loans.

The minister of foreign affairs, Zamocona, proposed a remedy that had been suggested several times by Ocampo, by Mata, by Miguel Lerdo de Tejada. Always, until now, Juárez had refused to consider it. This time he bowed to necessity. On July 17, 1861, he issued a decree temporarily suspending payment on the foreign debts for two years. With the revenues thus saved, the country could be pacified, roads could be opened, the people put to work. Trade would begin again. If England, France, and Spain would only be a little patient, they would be paid in full in good time.

But this is exactly what the foreign governments would not do. They had been waiting for this moment to make Mexico a colony again. The French minister, Saligny, broke off relations with Mexico. Spain did the same. England suspended diplomatic relations; her government had not quite decided what to do. The bold and necessary action of Benito Juárez had given them all the excuse to attack the Republic. Spain longed to get her colony back. Napoleon III of France had dreams of a conquest of his own. And England simply wanted her money back.

The United States was invited to join in the planned intervention but Abraham Lincoln refused. In fact, Lincoln's sympathy for Juárez was strengthened by the threat of foreign intervention. Beyond his refusal to ally himself with the invaders, the President of the United States, in the midst of a civil war of his own, could do nothing. The government in Mexico City was left to fight for its own survival.

A newspaper article reprinted from the New York *Tribune* called the intervention by England, France, and Spain "the most monstrous enterprise ever chronicled in modern history." The author, Karl Marx, then the *Tribune*'s London correspondent, ridiculed England's claim that her only interest was "peace-keeping" and "stabilizing" the Mexican government. "The oddest means ever hit on for consolidation of a government," Marx concluded, "consists of the seizure of its territory and the withholding of its revenues!" The article set off wide discussion in England and opposition to the intervention mounted. The changing opinion was important.

While Juárez and his ministers were attempting to deal with the crisis, Ortega went after Márquez. He managed to disperse the outlaws; but the Tiger of Tacubaya escaped capture again. Nevertheless, Ortega's small victory gave Juárez the opportunity to negotiate with the envoys of England and Spain.

General Juan Prim y Prats, Spain's representative in the capital, was personally friendly to the Juárez government. He made a strong plea for a peaceful settlement, but the Spanish ships carrying 6,000 soldiers continued to crowd Veracruz Harbor.

When the Spanish soldiers—the interventionists—in Veracruz asked for safe conduct to move to a healthier climate along the coast, Juárez sent Doblado to negotiate with them.

In Feburary 1862, the negotiations were successful. Juárez's conditions were met. The Spanish and British commissioners agreed to recognize the constitutional government and to respect its sovereignty. The Spanish and British invaders were ordered back to their ships and a few weeks later sailed for Europe. On the high seas they passed a French fleet bringing 10,000 battle-ready soldiers, the best of Napoleon's army.

The envoy of Napoleon III of France would sign no agreement. The Emperor's plan of conquest was brought into the daylight.

Juárez saw that the peace, won with such sacrifice, was shattered.

"Don't worry," he said quietly. "I still hope for a reasonable settlement. Mexico will survive!"

He summoned the nation to the defense of independence.

Meanwhile, Márquez was raiding around Puebla. Miramón and General Juan Nepomuceno Almonte had landed on Mexican soil. Other reactionary exiles were returning on every French ship that put into port.

Juárez issued a proclamation explaining the desperate situation to the people. The Mexican people were again facing their old enemies of the revolution plus a new one, the formidable French army. "We must now prove to France and to the entire world," he declared, "that we are worthy to be free."

Almonte held Juárez in special contempt for his Zapotec ancestry. He issued an appeal to Mexican traitors to join with the French in forming a new government "better suited to their needs and their religious beliefs."

The French general also answered Juárez's proclamation with one of his own. He asserted that the French flag had come to Mexico to stay and could be attacked only at great peril. Thus the old enemy and the new formed a compact to make sure that "the rich and the privileged should be on top and the poor on the bottom." Nothing would be changed from the days of New Spain, except the names of the masters. On April 19, 1862, Almonte declared himself president, but the power would be shared among Almonte, the Archbishop, and Saligny, minister of France.

Juárez's answer was to send Porfirio Díaz of Oaxaca with an army of 4,000 patriots to occupy the city of Puebla. Toward this fortified stronghold, Márquez's band of outlaws and a French army of 6,000 men were marching.

For a month the battle raged. Besieged and besiegers alike knew its importance. The citizens of Puebla, up to now, had bowed willingly to the Church authorities. But no longer! Not with independence at stake . . . and not against a foreign enemy. With Díaz and General Zaragoza, a newcomer from the north, the citizens turned back three attacks of the enemy. On May 5, 1862, the French and rebel forces were compelled to retreat with Díaz's troops at their heels. The ragged Mexican army had beaten the most powerful and famous troops in the world.

Not all the bitter, uneven struggle of the seven

years to come could blot out the memory of this victory. The Fifth of May (*Cinco de Mayo*) is today a national holiday in Mexico, comparable in importance to the United States' Fourth of July, second only in the eyes of Mexicans to September 16, 1810, the day Padre Hidalgo first raised the cry of independence.

❧16❧

Maximilian and Carlota

A year later, at sunset on May 31, 1863, President Juárez stood on the palace balcony overlooking the Zócalo. At his side were all his cabinet ministers. His wife and older children were just inside the great hall, unseen by the crowds below. The glass door was open and Juárez gathered strength from their presence.

The closing session of the Congress had adjourned that afternoon after hearing the president's decision to withdraw from the capital.

"Adversity," he said to the Congress, "dismays only contemptible peoples; our people are ennobled by great deeds, and the country has far from lost the enormous material and moral obstacles that it will place in the way of its unjust invaders. . . . Great has been the reverse that we have suffered, but greater are our constancy and resolution, and we shall fight on with the greater ardor and with the certainty that victory will be ours, no matter what may be the elements on which the enemy may count because the nation still has life and strong sons to defend her."

The nation still has life! During the year that had gone by since the glorious victory at Puebla, its very existence had been repeatedly threatened. Napoleon's answer to the events of Cinco de Mayo had been to send 20,000 more troops over the ocean. Storms and the fever-ridden marshes around Veracruz had delayed the French for some time and given Generals Zaragoza and Díaz a few months to gather armies of defense. Then in September 1862, Zaragoza, an immensely able commander, had died in Puebla of typhoid fever.

When the French army marched again toward Puebla, in the early spring of 1863, the traitor Márquez had moved to join them from the north.

Against this double threat, Díaz and Ortega again directed the defense of Puebla. For two long months they stood against the huge besieging army. The civilians and the soldiers in the city were starving. Their ammunition was almost gone.

The man entrusted with the task of getting supplies through was Ignacio Comonfort! He had begged to be permitted to return from exile to help in the defense of the government he had once betrayed. Juárez, never one to bear a grudge, had welcomed Comonfort and had given him command of 2,000 troops. However, on the way to Puebla, he was overtaken and defeated by Márquez. Most of his troops were killed or taken captive. Comonfort escaped, only to die later on the battlefield.

The anniversary of the victory of a year before found Puebla still in government hands; but less than two weeks later, without food or water or ammunition, Díaz and Ortega were forced to surrender the city. The French ordered all the officers of the conquered army sent under guard to Veracruz to be imprisoned.

Rumor reached the capital that many had already escaped. But Díaz was in the dungeon at Veracruz. And the fall of Puebla had opened the way for the invaders. They were marching toward the capital.

At first Juárez had considered putting up a fight for Mexico City, but he realized that he did not have enough guns or soldiers for a successful defense. The freedom of a country did not depend on possession of one city; it lay, he said, in the will of the people to defend their constitution. The only possible course was to withdraw. The president and the cabinet would make its way that night to a new seat of government in the city of San Luis Potosí, about 150 miles to the north. With all these events in mind the president could still say, "The nation has life."

At sundown Juárez stood on the balcony to watch the flag of the Mexican Republic lowered from the flagstaff above the National Palace. The plaza was a solid mass of silent people. The troops presented arms.

The national anthem was played, slowly, solemnly.

When the red, green, and white flag of Independence came down, it was handed to Juárez. The president raised it to his lips and cried out, "Viva Mexico!"

That night, under cover of darkness, a line of shabby black carriages, bearing the president and his family and all the members of his cabinet, drove out of Mexico City. Last in the procession came a lumbering wooden cart in which were stored a copy of the Constitution, the flag, and all the other valuable documents of the government. The troops that had come to defend the capital were dispersed around the countryside to cover the president's withdrawal.

On June 10, the French army marched in and took possession of Mexico City. At the head of the glittering parade, by the side of the French general, rode three Mexicans back from exile—Miramón, Almonte, and a priest in black robes, Padre Miranda. Ever since they had been exiled by the people, they had lived in France, planning and plotting for this day.

The imperial flag of Emperor Napoleon III flew from the palace flagstaff. Padre Miranda smiled to himself when he saw the Napoleonic crown and eagle and serpent fluttering in the breeze. If all went well, the French flag would soon take second place. Mexico would have an emperor of her own—a genuine ruler of royal blood, with a flag older than Bonaparte's. The groundwork of the plot had been laid in France and Austria. It was to prepare the way for a foreign emperor that the three Mexicans had crossed the ocean again. Meanwhile, let the French army subdue the Mexican people, let the French general repeat that the French flag of the Bonapartes had come to stay! Padre Miranda knew better . . .

It had been hard for Juárez to recognize France as the enemy of a free Mexico. From Miguel Méndez long ago, from Ocampo in the days of the New Orleans exile, from young Collin who had died for the idea of freedom in Mexico's civil war, from his own wide reading, Benito Juárez had come to look with love upon the French Revolution of 1789. But the France of 1860 was not the France of the Revolution. The French Republic had given way to the Empire, and empires are rooted in greed and arrogance and a hunger for power, at the expense of weaker peoples.

The plot against the Republic of Mexico had been long in the making, at first by Mexicans themselves. In 1854 Santa Anna, about to go into exile in Cuba, had commissioned a deposed aristocrat living in Paris to "shop around for a European prince of royal blood to become monarch of Mexico," one who would restore lost privileges to the landowners and army and clergy. Santa Anna's friend, Guttiérez de Estrada, gathered other exiles around him and traveled from court to court in this quest.

The likeliest candidate was a young prince of the

ancient line of Hapsburg kings. Archduke Maximilian of Austria, a brother of the Emperor Franz Joseph of Austria, was handsome, charming—everything a reigning monarch should be. In 1859, Guttiérez de Estrada and Padre Miranda managed to get an audience with the young man and offered him the crown of Mexico. He refused. Undaunted, the exiled Mexicans kept talking of monarchy. It was insufferable that the country should be governed by an Indian from Guelatao.

In 1860, they approached Maximilian again. The Archduke seemed content to lead a sheltered life at the Castle of Miramar, which Franz Joseph had built for him when he married into the royal family of Belgium. He had a long life ahead and the family would somehow provide a suitable throne somewhere in Europe. Maximilian collected butterflies and paintings and beautiful statues to adorn Miramar, and seemed without ambition.

However, his wife, barely out of her teens, had enough ambition for two. She was the daughter of a king and her older sister was Empress of France. And she, Carlota, much brighter and prettier and livelier than the Empress, was only an archduchess! When she learned that the European powers were intervening with armies in Mexico, the Mexican crown became suddenly quite desirable.

The plan of the Mexican exiles reached Napoleon III's wife with the suggestion "Why merely collect debts from Mexico when a French protectorate over the country could be established and her sister and her Hapsburg husband put on a throne?"

The Hapsburgs had worn crowns for centuries. Napoleon III of France was only on a throne because he was the nephew of Napoleon the Great. There was no royal blood in the family, and his claim to a crown could not be stretched farther back than fifty years. To have a Hapsburg beholden to a Napoleon for his title would make up for many snubs. Besides, Mexico had great natural resources. In proper hands the country would be a source of wealth. Napoleon III was willing to finance the project if Maximilian and his wife, Carlota, were willing to leave Europe and go to live in the barbaric country.

Late in 1862 the Mexican royalists again approached Maximilian, this time with the blessing of the Emperor and Empress of France. Carlota was in favor of accepting at once. Maximilian, who like Juárez was a reader of French works on liberty and democracy, made one condition. He would accept the crown only on the invitation of the people of Mexico.

Father Miranda, Almonte, and Miramón rushed home to prepare the way for an empire, and to arrange a vote that would convince Maximilian that he was wanted. In addition to his duties of subduing a stubborn people, the French commander-in-chief, General Achille Bazaine, was given the duty of concocting an invitation from the people of Mexico to Maximilian and Carlota to come to rule over them. To rule over liberty-loving millions whose elected president had established the seat of government in San Luis Potosí and was raising new armies to guard the independence they had won! Díaz had escaped from prison and was moving from village to village getting volunteers for the army.

To change the form of government seemed impossible, but a few chosen notables cast their vote for an empire. A few Indian bandits like Márquez, a few displaced soldiers like Miramón, some priests and monks (though not all), and the owners of large estates registered their acceptance. No one thought of asking the Indians who composed 80 per cent of the Mexican population. However, Maximilian was satisfied.

In early summer of 1863, Maximilian and Carlota were duly crowned Emperor and Empress of Mexico. The ceremonies took place in France at the court of Napoleon III. The royal couple then paid a visit to London and then to Rome to get the blessing of the Pope and finally, almost a year later, on the Austrian frigate *Novara* they set sail for Mexico. It was true that the French army had not yet won control of "their" country. There were still a few cities to be captured, French General Bazaine confided to Napoleon. And the "little Indian" still persisted in calling himself the president.

The news of the coronation came to San Luis Potosí from London. Juárez and his family were living very comfortably in the beautiful little city ringed by mountains that reminded them of home. Manuela, his oldest daughter, had married Pedro Santacilla, the young Cuban who had shared Juárez's exile in New Orleans. Santacilla had become the self-appointed guardian of the family and relieved Juárez's mind of many small anxieties. The large ones he had to face alone.

Crisis after crisis rose in the cabinet, and there had been many changes. Comonfort was now Minister of War, but in the same month that Maximilian was crowned Emperor, Comonfort left the seat of government with a small escort to confer with one of the commanders about a new campaign. He was ambushed by Márquez's bandits and assassinated.

"I cannot express to you all the pain that has been caused by this misfortune," Juárez wrote to his envoy, Romero, in Washington. "It is a great tragedy to lose a man, who, whatever one thinks may have been his political errors, was at the present time dedicated to the defense of the country."

It now seemed necessary to limit the defense to guerrilla warfare. One by one the central cities had been occupied by the overwhelming might of the French army. Morelia, Guanajuato, and Guadalajara were gone. No one knew when a French force would appear outside San Luis Potosí and try to occupy it.

In November, Juárez sent Margarita and the children in Santacilla's care to the village of Saltillo, near Monterrey. Saltillo was ninety miles distant. The trail, for it could scarcely be called a road, was through a canyon between barren mountains.

The best transportation Santacilla could find was a large cart drawn by two mules. When he drew up to the door, ready for the journey, Juárez had just received a packet of European mail. He opened the letter from London telling of the coronation of Maximilian ...

"I have a letter containing curious news," he said to his wife as she was about to say good-by. That was the only comment the president made. Parting from Margarita was of more immediate concern to him than the news that Napoleon had set up a puppet emperor on a nonexistent throne.

A month later a large force of French and Mexicans were on the way to take San Luis Potosí. Díaz, trying to stop them, was severely defeated. Again carriages were made ready and Juárez and the members of the cabinet quietly drove into the canyon toward Saltillo, the archives in a mule cart trailing behind.

The retreat from San Luis Potosí was serious for the morale of the government. As the sad little procession neared Saltillo, a delegation sent by Doblado came to meet Juárez. The president must be very tired, they said. Perhaps he would like to lay aside the burden of government and retire. General Ortega, the vice-president, could take over the office. Doblado, the delegation explained, was making no demands. He would support Juárez whatever his decision.

Juárez had to think fast. He had reason to doubt the loyalty of two of his generals—Ortega, because he was impatient when things were going badly, and Vidaurri, into whose territory they were now moving. Doblado was very influential. If he joined with the doubters, the outlook for the government could be dark indeed. Juárez did not give an inch.

"Far from being wearied," he answered, "I am as determined as I was six years ago when this struggle began. My conscience and my honor counsel me that it is my duty to keep the power that the vote of the nation confided in me."

His answer restored Doblado's confidence and he joined Juárez in Saltillo with a force of 1,500 men.

The reunion with his family in Saltillo was especially happy because during his stay there a son, Antonio, was born. But, in so small, so remote a place, Juárez could not keep his hands on the many threads of government. The city of Monterrey would be more suitable.

With Doblado's force as escort, he moved the government to Monterrey. Juárez had notified Governor Vidaurri of his intention, but when he arrived in Monterrey, the expected trouble with the governor came to a head. Juárez firmly established himself in the state house and Vidaurri threatened to attack. Vidaurri was now at last in open rebellion.

Juárez returned to Saltillo and stationed all the forces he had on the road between Monterrey and Saltillo. Vidaurri had been negotiating with the French and now proposed to let the people of the district vote between "peace" (meaning surrender to the French) or "war" (meaning support for Juárez). The vote was held. Almost all the votes were for "war." Juárez had won another battle. Vidaurri retired to private life, but eventually he was to join the forces of intervention.

Juárez led the government solemnly into Monterrey. A month later he sent for his family. While in Monterrey a baby girl was born to Manuela—Juárez's and his wife's first grandchild. But the family would not be together for long. By the end of May 1864, Juárez was thinking that it might be wise to arrange to send his family to the United States for the duration of the war.

The Civil War to the north had reached a turning point, and though Lincoln had been able to do little in a material way for Mexico's independence, his sympathy and understanding had never wavered. Juárez did not ask for more.

"It is enough for us if the North destroys slavery and does not recognize Maximilian," he had said to Margarita when he broke the news of his decision to send the family to the United States. It was no longer safe for them in Mexico. The war was going very badly and Maximilian and Carlota had landed on Mexican soil.

Almost a year had gone by since the royal couple had accepted the Mexican crown, a year spent making state visits to the courts of Europe. Emperor Franz Joseph of Austria had visited them at Miramar, taking the final precaution of having his younger brother sign a paper renouncing all claim to the throne of Austria. It did not matter to Maximilian and Carlota. Their empire was across the ocean. And they were very busy choosing tapestries and gilded furniture, glittering chandeliers, red-velvet draperies, harpsichords, and other little luxuries suitable for a royal palace.

On the six weeks' voyage across the Atlantic, Maximilian had occupied himself with writing a manual of court etiquette while Carlota dreamed romantic dreams of the country she thought of as "her Mexico."

As they neared sight of land, Maximilian had an idea. Much as the Mexicans aboard had ridiculed and vilified the dark-skinned Indian president, Maximilian could not help but admire Juárez. Why not write him a letter, graciously inviting him to a conference in the imperial palace to settle their differences and so make peace in the nation? Maximilian considered himself very broad-minded and democratic. He would find some unimportant post for this courageous old Indian at his court.

Juárez received the letter at Monterrey while the Emperor and Empress were being escorted on the road between Veracruz and Mexico City. It was the same road Benito Juárez had traveled with Margarita at his side through enraptured crowds for the victorious return to the capital in 1861. The foreigners —unconsciously Juárez used the old Zapotec word for the new invaders—the foreigners would drive for part of the way along his unfinished railroad. "When will we ever finish it?" Juárez asked himself as he broke the seal of Maximilian's letter. Not "if," even in these dark days, but "when" . . .

That night by candlelight, he wrote his answer to Maximilian's invitation:

> *I write in great haste and without a meditated editing, because you must realize that the delicate and important duties of President of the Republic absorb all my time, without permitting me to rest at night. . . . I propose nevertheless, to answer the principal points of your letter. . . . You tell me that, abandoning succession to a throne in Europe, forsaking your family, your friends, your fortune and, what is most dear to a man, your country, you have come with your wife, Doña Carlota, to distant and unknown lands to satisfy the summons spontaneously made by a people that rest their felicity and their future in you. . . . You invite me to go to*

Mexico City to which you are bound . . . it is impossible for me to accept your summons, sir; my occupations do not allow it. . . . It is true, sir, that contemporary history records the names of great traitors who have broken their oaths and their promises and failed their own party and all that is sacred to a man of honor . . . but the present incumbent of the Presidency of the Republic who has sprung from the obscure mass of people will not succumb. . . . It is given to men, sir, to attack the rights of others, to take their property, to attempt to take the lives of those who defend their liberty . . . but there is one thing which is beyond perversity, and that is the tremendous verdict of history. History will judge us. I am your obedient servant,

Benito Juárez.

17

The Turning Point

Maximilian and Carlota proceeded to set up court in Mexico City—not in the National Palace, however. Carlota found the gloomy old building unsuitable. For the royal residence, Carlota chose the hilltop fortress of Chapultepec. The castle was set in a spacious park at the far end of the capital city. She had the building remodeled as best she could, to receive the furnishings she had brought from Europe.

Coachbuilders were put to work creating a high-wheeled gilded carriage such as Napoleon and *his* empress used on the broad avenues of Paris. But Mexico City was not Paris. It sprawled over its wide plateau, its streets, except around the Zócalo, were narrow and winding. There was no tree-lined Champs Élysée where the gilded carriage and its occupants could be seen and admired. Carlota ordered houses torn down, grass and trees and flowers planted along Calle Alameda, which stretched from the National Palace all the way to Chapultepec Castle. When completed, the Alameda was one long magnificent boulevard, almost like the Champs Élysée. The gilded carriage drawn by four black horses could now give the Mexican people a proper impression of royalty.

"We considered it necessary," Carlota explained sweetly to the French commander-in-chief who complained of the expense. Money was no problem to the Emperor and Empress, because for these first years Napoleon had guaranteed the whole cost of the expedition.

At the castle, Carlota patiently taught the Mexican ladies-in-waiting to curtsy before walking out backwards from her imperial presence and other matters of court etiquette. But the days were long because Maximilian went every morning to the National Palace to "govern." Carlota's favorite moment of the day was when she stood at the castle window and gazed down the long, beautiful vistas of the Alameda for the first glimpse of her husband returning home.

Empress Carlota was just twenty-two years old, living out a fantasy in a girl's dream world. She no longer spoke of "my Mexico" because the French were so very slow in pacifying the stubborn inhabitants. Travel outside the capital was not safe; but this broad avenue of beauty, this Alameda at least, was her creation. The rest would follow.

Maximilian, too, was play-acting at governing. He sat at his desk in the National Palace all day making lists of the things he wanted to do for "his" people. He was very well meaning, but the people who had brought him into Mexico were not. He infuriated the Archbishop and Padre Miranda by putting back into effect the *Ley Juárez* and other reform laws regulating the civil power of the Church authorities. He did nothing to restore their valuable properties which Juárez's government had stolen. Nothing? He did worse than nothing. He talked about religious liberty and cultivated such traitors as Urago and Vidaurri, whom the French had bribed into leaving Juárez's army.

The Emperor was thoroughly disappointing to the Mexican exiles. They had waited so long and worked so hard for a return to yesterday . . . They were bitter at the French, too. When Santa Anna, who might have talked sense to the Emperor, came over from Cuba, it was the French who ordered him deported almost as soon as he had landed.

If everything was not going as well as expected in Mexico City, Juárez's position was infinitely worse. In August 1864, he realized that Monterrey could no longer be held by his government. Where the next stopping place would be, he did not know, except that as long as he was alive it would be somewhere in Mexico. But Margarita and the family must leave at once. Pedro Santacilla quietly made the final arrangements.

On the day before the departure, Juárez took his

wife to a dressmaker's shop and gave her the dress he had ordered as a surprise. It was brocade, with silver buttons down the front of the blouse and a wide hoop-skirt. Margarita had not had a new dress in three years. Two more years were to pass in exile and sorrow before she would wear the dress her husband had chosen for her. Two years! While her beloved husband was driven from one part of his country to another!

Juárez accompanied his family to the next village and watched them drive off in a cloud of dust across the vast, sparsely inhabited barren country toward a foreign land.

"I have brought her nothing but sorrow," Benito Juárez said to himself as he walked back alone to take up the burdens of government. But this was not true, The Indian patriot, twenty years older than his pretty wife, had given Margarita his whole heart.

Two weeks later news came that a French army was within four days' march of Monterrey. Juárez had only one battalion of soldiers in the town. Doblado and Ortega had lost heart, disbanded their armies and left for the United States. Díaz had held Oaxaca for months, but just a week ago he had been defeated and was hiding in the mountains until it was safe to return. Juan Álvarez in the state of Guerrero still held open the port of Acapulco to receive arms from the United States. But what use were arms when the government-on-the-run had no soldiers or money to support an army?

There was no spot on Mexican soil where the government would be safe from attack except in the extreme north in the state of Chihuahua. A desert waste separated the state from the rest of Mexico. The French army with its elaborate equipment would bog down in the desert sand, but the "government in a carriage" could get through. "One carriage will be enough," Juárez said sadly to his cabinet. "There are only four of us left."

Firing had already broken out in the streets of Monterrey between turncoat Mexicans and the government defenders on the day set for departure. Juárez was eating his noonday meal when a messenger came to ask him to hurry. The carriage was waiting, the constitution, the now bedraggled flag, and the archives were stowed in the mule cart.

"The president must not seem to run away," Juárez said, as he went on eating. "The government must move, it is true, but it must move with dignity."

Lerdo de Tejada, Iglesias, and Prieto, his ministers of state, were in the carriage when Juárez appeared. They drove off in a spatter of bullets, several of which struck the sides of the vehicle.

The battalion covered their retreat from Monterrey, but on the long journey north the government was without escort. The people in scattered huts in the desert fed the president and his party. Of their devotion to Juárez there could be no doubt. In one isolated village the inhabitants unhitched the horses and would have drawn the bullet-riddled carriage themselves if Juárez had not forbidden it as unworthy of a free and equal people.

Juárez's destination was the capital city of Chihuahua. After almost a month's travel, the party came to this green and welcoming town. The house prepared for them stood open day and night. His friends warned the president to keep his doors closed.

"What can they do to us?" he asked.

"But you should be careful, Don Benito."

"Of whom?"

"Of the enemy."

"Why? We are going to win in the end. You will see!"

Letters he had anxiously waited for came from New York at last. All was well, Margarita wrote. Then sorrowful letters, sorrowful beyond bearing. Pepe, the most brilliant and charming of all his children, was dead of an unknown sickness. Juárez sank into a profound sadness for his own loss and for Margarita.

Months afterward at a dinner to celebrate his birthday, someone proposed a toast to the health of his family. Juárez rose to respond. He had tears in his eyes.

"I see the country here and I say to it solemnly that my own sacrifice is nothing, that the sacrifice of my family would be much, would be infinite for me. But if need be, so be it. Viva Mexico!"

"Where is Juárez?" people asked when Chihuahua became too dangerous a refuge. The government had to move again, this time to the farthest village on the banks of the Rio Grande within sight of the state of Texas.

An old man in Mexico City answered. "Where is he? I do not know the name of the line of land that he occupies at this moment. But he is in the Republic, he works for the Republic and will die in the Republic. If only one corner of the country is left, there you will be sure to find the president."

And where were Maximilian, the Emperor, and his wife, Carlota? Still holding court in an alien land, under the protection of 30,000 French troops in their bright red pants and gold braid.

"Poor Maximilian!" one of the French generals said. "What are you doing in this land, with an army that has shed its blood to put you on a throne? The army will leave and then? Poor fool! You will regret your fine castle of Miramar."

While the United States had been locked in a struggle for its own survival, its government could not afford to make demands of the French Emperor. Arms and a few volunteers had entered across the border, especially after the Confederacy sent an envoy to the court of Maximilian. But the United States was at peace in 1866. Lincoln was dead, but the sympathy he had expressed for Juárez was widespread in the North, especially among the generals. Generals Grant and Schofield had elaborate plans for raising 15,000 volunteers if Juárez wanted them.

Juárez desired no more intervention, even on his own side. More valuable was the warning sent to Napoleon III by Secretary of State Seward early in 1866: "The United States has not seen any satisfactory evidence that the people of Mexico had called into being the so-called empire. The withdrawal of French troops is deemed necessary. . . ."

Napoleon III was already discouraged with his Mexican adventure, and the refusal of Juárez to acknowledge defeat. He was having difficulties with the German state of Prussia. Seward's note was just one more thing. But Seward also sent General Sheridan, a strong supporter of Juárez's cause, to the Texas border with 100,000 men of the regular United States Army. They did not plan to enter Mexico, but they were there, ready if needed. Care was taken that Napoleon III should hear of Sheridan's presence.

In April 1866, two years after Maximilian and Carlota set sail from Europe, the Emperor of France issued orders to evacuate Mexico. The first detachment of the French army sailed from Veracruz for home in November. Juárez, waiting in an adobe house in Paso del Norte, was reminded of something Abraham Lincoln had said at the very beginning of Maximilian's entry into Mexico. "When the French army is gone, Benito Juárez will take care of Maximilian."

∾18∾

"*The People to Juárez*"

Benito Juárez sat at his desk in the little house in Paso del Norte, now called Ciudad Juárez. Twenty-four years had gone by since sixteen-year-old Margarita Maza had said of him, "He is very homely, but he is very good." In 1866, Juárez had become a symbol of goodness, a symbol of honest homeliness, too, in contrast to the gaudy empire of Maximilian and Carlota. He was like a granite boulder against which ocean waves beat in vain.

Now the storms he had withstood were quieting. The tide was going out. As the French army evacuated city after city, the republicans swarmed in. With guns General Sheridan declared "surplus" and had his soldiers dump at night across the river onto the Mexican shore, Chihuahua had been retaken. More guns appeared with every dawn and supporters of Juárez could help themselves to the treasure. Long wagon trains loaded with arms plodded across the desert with the Mexicans who now poured into recruiting stations.

Messages came to Juárez that Guerrero was cleared of the enemy. Díaz was in such absolute control of Oaxaca that he could set up a civil government and move out with his army, ready to liberate Puebla and the capital when the last of the French had re-embarked. Doblado was back in the field and had raised troops to free Saltillo and Monterrey.

Romero wrote from Washington that General Grant had opened a recruiting office. "Grant could not do more if he were a Mexican," Romero added. But Juárez was never anxious for foreign soldiers. "With time and our tenacious resistance we shall wear out the enemy without foreign assistance, and that is the greatest glory I desire for my country."

The admirers of Juárez in Washington found another way to honor him. In March 1866, Margarita had come from New York City to nurse Romero's mother who was sick. Doña Margarita's presence in the capital of the United States was turned into a state visit of the wife of the head of a government. Seward gave a large dinner; President Johnson, a reception at the White House; General Grant gave a ball.

Margarita had never recovered from her despair over the death of Pepe. A few weeks before coming to Washington, calamity had struck again. Antonio, the baby born in Saltillo, the little boy who had never known his father, had also died. She had no heart for gaiety, but had accepted all these invitations because she knew that the attention sprang from the affection and sympathy felt for her husband.

When she was about to return to New York, she wrote Juárez and enclosed a newspaper clipping in her letter.

> *The night before last* [she wrote], *Romero took me to President Johnson's reception and as you will see in the* Herald *they say I was elegantly dressed, with many diamonds. That's not true. All of my elegance consisted of the dress you bought me in Monterrey. . . . Having had so many cares and sorrows, I had not worn the special dress before. And as for the diamonds, I wore no more than some earrings you gave me once on my Saint's day. . . . I tell you all this because they shall not say that when you were suffering every privation in El Paso I was here enjoying luxury. . . . I shall have peace only when I am with you. . . .*

She longed to go home to share the hardships with him, but Juárez said that the time had not yet come. The evacuation of the French was dragging on. With every shipload returning to France, Maximilian and Carlota sent messages of violent protest to Napoleon. Almonte went in person to try to keep the soldiers in Mexico. Napoleon answered Almonte that he could no longer spare 20,000 soldiers, nor 10,000, nor even one. It might be best, he said, for Maximilian to abdicate.

Give up the dream of empire? Maximilian was willing. Perhaps they would be allowed to become ordinary Mexican citizens, to settle down in a pretty town like Cuernavaca where the butterflies . . . Carlota would not hear of it. The Empress rode to Veracruz in her gilded carriage and demanded passage in the last vessel carrying French soldiers. She and her husband were, after all, related to every crowned head in Europe. She would explain their situation and return with a fresh army.

Carlota never saw Mexico again. She begged, she demanded, she went down on her knees to her royal relatives. They felt sorry for her—who would not? But they would do nothing.

The Pope in Rome was her last hope. The Pope received her coldly. Reports of Maximilian's religious toleration had come to the Vatican from Mexico. The Archbishop had written that the Emperor and Empress were no more useful to the Mexican church than Juárez.

In all her sheltered life Carlota had never known failure. Now, when she saw defeat closing in, reason deserted her. She was confined in the castle of Miramar, knowing nothing, remembering nothing for all the years of her long life. She lived on, into the twentieth century and died at last in 1927.

The news of Carlota's breakdown came to her husband in the encampment of his Mexican army. The soldiers of Márquez, of Tomás Mejía, of Miramón were at last the Emperor's to command. For a brief time they managed to win a few engagements, then, at Querétaro, a few miles from the capital, General Escobedo forced the surrender of the enemy. Márquez escaped capture as usual and, with Vidaurri, prepared to defend Mexico City. But Miramón, Mejía, and Emperor Maximilian were taken prisoner.

Maximilian at last declared himself willing to abdicate and to leave the country forever. General Escobedo answered that the prisoner's request would be referred to the proper authorities. Two days later, by order of Benito Juárez, Mejía, Miramón, and Maximilian were tried by court-martial. The verdict for all three was death by a firing squad.

In the weeks before the battle of Querétaro, Juárez had made his way out of the north and established the seat of government once more at San Luis Potosí. The lawyer who had volunteered to defend the Emperor at his trial was himself a devoted liberal whose son was in the republican forces. He rushed to Juárez to request that Maximilian's life be spared.

Benito Juárez faced one of the hardest decisions of his life. He was not one to make up his mind on the spur of the moment. There was much to be said on both sides. His first duty was to postpone the executions set for dawn the next morning. A message to General Escobedo took care of that. The rest was more difficult. His own hesitancy at taking a human life was balanced against the necessity for equal treatment under the law. The law, under which the three prisoners were convicted, applied equally to all three. Juárez had signed the decree himself at the beginning of the French intervention. The law prescribed the penalty of death for foreigners conspiring against Mexican independence and for Mexicans assisting them. Should Maximilian get special privileges? Or Miramón? Or Mejía, whose life Juárez had spared once before?

At that time he had granted clemency at the plea of the wife of his friend Leandro Valle. Something Juárez said at that time may have crossed his mind again, as he paced the floor in the night.

"With this reprieve I may be signing the death warrant of hundreds of innocent men."

His words had proved prophetic, for Mejía had come back to the country to fight and to kill.

There was another incident buried deeper in Juárez's memory: the exchange between Ocampo and Collin, the young Frenchman. Ocampo and Collin were both dead, but Ocampo's words lived on—"Taking the life of one man has saved the lives of many."

Maximilian, alive, could do more mischief. Not because he was brutal or warlike, but because he allowed himself to be used for brutal ends. Having known no other life than the courts of kings, he considered himself above human law.

Pleas for clemency for Maximilian came to Juárez from all over the world. From those more guilty than

the prisoner and from noble people Juárez admired—
from Garibaldi of Italy, from Victor Hugo of France.
But Benito Juárez had to decide all alone in terms of
justice and the nation's good. He refused to veto the
decision of the court-martial and five days after sen-
tence was passed, on June 19, 1867, Emperor Maximilian and the two Mexican traitors were shot.

"Poor Maximilian!" a French soldier had said when
the Emperor was in the height of his glory. He met
death bravely and many people wept at his burial.
Juárez sorrowed more for the calamities his adventure
had brought to Mexico. "The executions at Querétaro," he said, "were necessitated by the gravest mo-
tives of justice combined with the need for securing
the peace."

Peace! Díaz was besieging Mexico City, still held by
Márquez and Vidaurri. But the end was very near.
Juárez had sent for his family. Margarita and his children and Santacilla were on the high seas, coming
home by Veracruz.

With Maximilian dead, the imperialists surrendered
on June 21st. Márquez went into hiding. Vidaurri was
shot trying to escape. Most of the soldiers were
granted pardons. The people welcomed Porfirio Díaz
as a deliverer.

Juárez and his ministers were moving under military escort toward the capital. Their progress was
slow because in every town, at every crossroads, the

inhabitants gave Juárez an ovation. Death and fear were forgotten in wild rejoicing. They moved slowly, too, because their battered carriages kept breaking down, but Juárez would have no other vehicles.

Díaz had ridden north of the city to meet Juárez. They had breakfast together—the brave and victorious young general who had once been Juárez's pupil, and the aging, shabby president, son of the people he loved as if each were his brother. At Díaz's request, the government party stopped for a few days at the Chapultepec Castle which was still filled with Carlota's finery. Juárez would have preferred going quietly on to the city, but he understood preparations for his return to the capital were important and took time.

On July 15, Juárez and his handful of ministers entered Mexico City, still riding in the old carriage that had become a part of Mexican history. In a travel-stained suit the "little Indian" rode between garlands of flowers, to the din of trumpets, bells, and rockets; he rode down the broad avenue of blossoming trees from Chapultepec to the National Palace. Arches and banners across the Alameda and from every balcony proclaimed, "The People to Juárez."

The red, green, and white flag of independence and freedom flew from the roofs of every building except one. The flagstaff in front of the National Palace was bare. The president drove up to the palace door through a narrow passage left by massed troops, standing at attention.

Porfirio Díaz, remembering 1863, when the flag was lowered and entrusted to Juárez's care, had planned a surprise. In full-dress uniform, the soldier who had saved Oaxaca, had freed Puebla, and fought the final battle for Mexico City, left his troops and came forward. He presented a handsome new flag to Juárez who raised the colors to fly again over the palace. "Viva Juárez! Viva Mexico!" the people cheered.

The day of triumph was not quite over. The people had spoken to Juárez. He had not yet spoken to the people.

The president looked down at the thousands in the enormous plaza. He had been thinking all along the way what he should say to them. "You know our needs"—the thought of the men of Guelatao so long ago was echoed in the upturned, waiting faces. Peace, the people needed most of all. For ten years they had struggled under his guidance to build a free and independent nation. For forty-seven years before that time, since Hidalgo's first uprising in 1810 an independent Mexico had been their goal.

But what is peace? Not merely cessation from fighting. It was a time for coming together, for brotherhood.

Slowly and in simple language Benito Juárez shared his thoughts with the multitude. He closed his address to the nation with words that belong not to Mexico alone, but to all humanity:

"For nations as well as for individuals, respect for the rights of others is peace."

❧ 19 ❧
The Judgment of History

The United States government had offered the Juárez family a warship for the journey home. They steamed into the harbor of Veracruz on almost the same day that the president re-entered his capital. To the people of Veracruz the coming of Doña Margarita was an event in itself. They had not forgotten her walk through the wilderness with her children, nor her care for them and her courage under siege in the two years she had spent in their city. These things were in the minds of the people who crowded the streets to welcome her as warmly as the victory was being celebrated in Mexico City.

With flowers, banners, bells, and fireworks, all of Veracruz came down to the dock. It is said that the people also brought Empress Carlota's gilded coach, which had been left in Veracruz, for Margarita to ride in.

Then they saw her coming down the gangplank,

dressed in black, surrounded by her daughters and leaning on the arm of Bene, her only remaining son. Margarita was still beautiful and gracious, but all the gaiety they remembered was gone. The rumor swept through the subdued crowd that she had brought with her the coffins of her two dead sons. Pepe, who had walked the streets of Veracruz with Don Benito, and the little one, born in Saltillo . . .

The trumpets were silent; the fireworks stayed in their wrappers; the gilded coach stood forgotten on the side street. Veracruz paid Doña Margarita a tribute better than cheers and music—a tribute of love.

Ten days later, Margarita was at home with her husband in a house Díaz had found for the family. The president had rooms in the National Palace, but for him a palace was not a home where children could dance and sing and play their pieces on the piano. The perfect understanding and trust between Margarita and Benito Juárez was deepened, if possible, by the separation and suffering each one had experienced. Margarita was Juárez's other self. Now that she had come, he was a whole person again.

To complete the circle, Josefa came for a visit and the cares of state were put aside for a few days. The art of taking pictures with a camera was just being introduced in Mexico and the three of them, the president and the two women who loved him the most had a little tintype picture made. It hangs among the treasures in the National Palace to this day.

The respite from affairs of state was not for long. Juárez's term of office had expired while he was in the desert. Against the letter of the law, but of necessity, he had continued in office, ruling by decree. It worried him to have bypassed the Constitution and it cost him the support of friends such as Ramirez and even temporarily of Prieto. His first act on his return to the capital was to call an election.

In September 1867, Juárez was duly re-elected, but not without opposition by two of his most faithful supporters. General Díaz and Lerdo de Tejada ran against the president. Lerdo de Tejada was elected to the vice-presidency. Porfirio Díaz, feeling that his service to the country was not appreciated, retired to his farm in Oaxaca—a shadow of trouble ahead.

Many other problems called for Juárez's attention, but with his wife at his side no problem seemed insurmountable. He ran the government much as he had in Oaxaca. He persuaded Congress to pass a law making elementary education compulsory and free in the nation. Where everyone could vote, everyone must be able to learn to read.

With the help of Romero, Secretary of the Treasury, he found the money at last to finish the railroad to Veracruz and begin another railroad, to open the desert of the north.

But these things were just a beginning. The problem of the deep poverty of the Indian population was still unsolved. They needed land to farm and better houses and outlets for trade. The whole country needed ways to develop the great natural wealth underground. The men who opposed Juárez did not let him forget the things still undone. With his old optimism he said, "Don't worry. We will come to these matters in time."

But time was running out. Four years of comparative happiness and tranquility were left to him. In January 1871, death came abruptly and without warning to Margarita. Juárez was alone, and from that moment he was an old man.

Too old, many have said, to run for the presidency again! Yet, work was his only solace. He worked at the palace from morning until night and slept there in the rooms set aside for him.

Great pressure was brought on Juárez to seek out a younger man to support. Lerdo de Tejada and Porfirio Díaz were again the opposing candidates.

The business of peace was unfinished. Which of those two could be trusted to carry it through? If Lerdo de Tejada were elected, would Díaz accept the election? He had the whole military behind him; he was already encouraging open revolt. True, Porfiro Díaz was young, vigorous, and popular. But Juárez had begun to see in military power a threat to democracy almost as strong as had been the all-powerful Church ten years ago.

Against the judgment of his friends, against his own desire, Benito Juárez offered to serve "for the best interests of Mexico."

He won the election, but he lived less than a year. On July 17, 1872, he had an attack of angina pectoris, an extremely painful but not necessarily fatal condition of the heart. He had had attacks before which had scarcely interrupted his work. He would not stop now!

All the next day, between attacks, Juárez sat wrapped in a blanket, in the great, gloomy room in the palace. He received ministers of state who came asking questions.

His doctor and his daughters and son-in-law hovered near. Night came and Juárez sent the family to the dining room for their supper. He talked quietly to the doctor about his childhood in Guelatao.

Once he interrupted himself to ask, "Is my illness— fatal?"

The physician nodded. He knew that Benito Juárez would want the truth.

The dying man went on with his remembrances. The doctor, exhausted by the long vigil, dozed in his chair. Juárez picked up his book on French law and began to read.

Page 261 . . . *The French language was beautiful,* he thought to himself. *And France herself was once more a Republic . . .* Napoleon was deposed and many Frenchmen gave credit to Mexico's stand against intervention as the beginning of the overthrow of the Empire—and there was the tribute that had come from a friend of Garibaldi—a tribute to Juárez: "You, who rose from a humble toiler in the Sierra of Oaxaca to become the great laborer for liberty, civilization, and progress, you, who because of your deeds and your virtues have rightly been hailed the Lincoln of Mexico. . . ." He read to the bottom of the page.

There was the pain again! Juárez laid his book down on the blanket, open at page 262. He closed his eyes.

A few minutes later the doctor woke and realized that the president was dead.

Many biographies have been written, many legends told about the "little Indian" who was the master builder of the Mexican Republic. Many of the things that Juárez feared for his country came to pass. Many of his hopes wait fulfillment. But the dream he brought down the mountain as a boy, the dream of liberty and education, the dream of equality, is cemented into the very foundations of the nation.

"History will judge us," Juárez wrote in his letter to Maximilian. Today, people all over the world—in Asia, Africa, Latin America—are struggling against odds to build freedom for their own society, for their own nations. Benito Juárez's experience, his words preserved on painted walls in his native land have a universal meaning: "For nations, as well as for individuals, respect for the rights of others is peace."

Suggested Reading

Augur, Helen: *Zapotec*. New York: Doubleday & Company; 1954.

Baker, Nina Brown: *Juárez, Hero of Mexico*. New York: Vanguard Press, Inc.; 1942.

Bancroft, H. H.: *History of Mexico*. San Francisco: History Company; 1883–1888.

Calderon de la Barca, F. I.: *Life in Mexico During a Residence of Two Years in that Country*. New York: E. P. Dutton & Co., Inc.; 1931.

Gruening, Ernest Henry: *Mexico and its Heritage*. New York and London: The Century Company; 1928.

Lawrence, D. H.: *Mornings in Mexico*. New York: Alfred A. Knopf, Inc.; 1927.

Marx, Karl and Friederich Engels: *The Civil War in the United States*. Enmale, Richard (ed.). New York: International Publishers Co., Inc.; 1931.

* Moheno, Roberto: *Juárez ante Dios y ante los Hombres*. Mexico: Libres Mexico Editores; 1964.

Prescott, William H.: *History of the Conquest of Mexico and History of the Conquest of Peru.* Unabridged 4th edn. New York: Random House, Inc.; 1936.

* Prieto, Guillermo: *Lecciones de Historia Patria.* Mexico City: Editoria Nacional; 1901.

————: *Memorias de mis Tiempo.* Mexico City: Editoria Nacional; 1944.

————: *San Francisco as Viewed by a Mexican Exile.* San Francisco: J. H. Nash; 1938.

* Reza, Juan de Dios: *Benito Juárez.* Mexico City: Editoria Nacional; 1961.

Rives, George Lockhart: *The United States and Mexico, 1821–1848.* New York: Charles Scribner's Sons; 1913.

Roeder, Ralph: *Juárez and His Mexico, a biographical history.* 2 vols. New York: The Viking Press, Inc.; 1947.

Sandburg, Carl: *The Complete Life of Abraham Lincoln.* 1 vol. New York: Harcourt, Brace & World, Inc.; 1954.

* Sierra, Justo: *Juárez, Su Obra y Su Tiempo.* Mexico City: University of Mexico, new edn.; 1956.

Smart, Charles Allen: *Viva Juárez!* Philadelphia: J. B. Lippincott Co.; 1963.

(*) In Spanish

Index

ABOUT THE AUTHOR

Emma Gelders Sterne is the author of four previous, widely acclaimed biographies for Knopf: *Blood Brothers, Vasco Nuñez de Balboa, Mary McLeod Bethune,* and *I Have a Dream.*

She has been a teacher and editor, and for many years made her home in New England and New York. She now lives in San Jose, California.

Before writing *Benito Juárez,* Mrs. Sterne traveled extensively in Mexico. She spent time in Juárez's home village, as well as in the major cities, and talked to many people whose grandparents had actually known their well-loved hero.

The text of this book was set on the Linotype in Janson, a recutting made directly from type cast from matrices long thought to have been made by the Dutchman Anton Janson, who was a practicing type founder in Leipzig during the years 1668–87. However, it has been conclusively demonstrated that these types are actually the work of Nicholas Kis (1650–1702), a Hungarian, who most probably learned his trade from the master Dutch type-founder Kirk Voskens. The type is an excellent example of the influential and sturdy Dutch types that prevailed in England up to the time William Caslon developed his own incomparable designs from these Dutch faces. Design by Atha Tehon.